Maria's

Duck Tales

Wildlife stories from my garden

Maria Daddino

Llumina
Press

ISBN: 978-1-60594-341-1 (PB)

Printed in the United States of America by Llumina Press

Library of Congress Control Number: 2010915419

"... My garden of flowers is also my garden
of thoughts and dreams.
The thoughts grow as freely as the flowers,
And the dreams are as beautiful."

~ Abram L. Urban

◆◆◆

"All things bright and beautiful,
All creatures great and small,
All things wise and wonderful:
The Lord God made them all."

Each little flower that opens,
Each little bird that sings,
He made their glowing colors,
He made their tiny wings ..."

~ Cecil F. Alexander

To my sweet and delicious grandchildren

Those indomitable triplets

Julia, Luke and William

And little Matthew

The icing on the cake

Very special thanks to

Steve Ensign for his exquisite art work and
patience

Deborah Greenspan and her wonderful
staff at Llumina Press
for their encouragement and commitment

and

All of my "wild-friends" who fill each day
with joy and serenity!

Introduction

My garden is one of the great passions of my life. It is my sanctuary ... my refuge ... my shelter from the storms of life ... a haven where I am safe ... a place in which I dare to dream. It's simply just where I always want to be.

Yet, simply having a garden filled with magnificent native trees and shrubs, colorful, fragrant flowers, sun-kissed heirloom vegetables and deliciously aromatic herbs is only a part of what makes my garden so very special to me. For me to be truly happy, my garden must also be filled to overflowing with the magnificent songs of birds and the undulating flights of brightly colored butterflies. It must be home to ducks and deer, turkeys and pheasants, bunnies and foxes and great blue herons and osprey.

All creatures - be they furry or feathered - are most welcome in my private wildlife habitat for it is my "wild-friends" who have always been the true highlights of my garden. Their visits make my garden come alive. The bond that I share with these wild creatures and the joy that they bring to me is absolutely priceless.

The antics of my squirrels have brightened many a cloudy day, both figuratively and literally. A small opossum family was the highlight of some very special summer evening visits and the ducks, geese and swans of Penataquit Creek put smiles on my face and stories in my heart that will last me a lifetime.

◆◆◆

On cold winter evenings in my new home on the East End of Long Island, I thrill at the nightly visits of majestic bucks and beautiful does. A family of delightful turkeys entertained me all summer long, capturing my heart. And a chubby groundhog, named George, has, just in time for his long winter's nap, finished the construction of his "McMansion" in the middle of my herb garden. And, next year, I plan to celebrate my very own groundhog day. Who needs "Malverne Mel" or "Holbrook Hal" when I have "East Quogue George!"

◆◆◆

As I look back over the years, I don't quite know how I became "me." I grew up in Brooklyn in the 1940's and it was an extremely difficult childhood for me. I was an only child who was raised by two sets of parents – my own and a very dear aunt and uncle who had no children of their own and who considered me "theirs."

I was a reader … a dreamer … a child of nature who had never set foot in the country … raised in a "practical" home filled with "practical" plastic flowers … and a house in which no muddy paw prints were allowed on the always immaculate floors.

Yet, something undeniable in my soul longed for the soft, velvety feel of green grass under my bare feet, the sweet smell of roses and honeysuckle drifting in on warm summer breezes and the love and affection of a collie always beside me. The deep passion I felt for these things defied all logic.

On the barren cement streets of East New York, Brooklyn, where I spent my early years, the only "flowers" I knew grew through the cracks in the sidewalk. I lived in a row house with tiny gardens, both front and back, that, years before I was born, had been encased in cement.

A few scraggly trees unsuccessfully tried their very best to graciously line the narrow street on which I lived and, in front of my house, what could have been a stately maple tree, had it been properly cared for, suffered not only from a lack of love, but, also, from the indignity of every spring having its bark painted white by my dear Uncle Johnny. He used whatever leftover household paint that he could find totally unaware, back in those days, of the reason for painting tree trunks with homemade pesticide solutions. My family knew only that the tree looked "clean" when Uncle Johnny was done.

Is it any wonder that, as a little girl, I disobeyed my parents as often as I could, walking the two or so miles from my home to Highland Park where I delightedly basked in the warm sunshine and listened to the soothing sounds of the birds? It was here, where I contentedly enjoyed the serene simplicity of nature, that my life-long love affair with birds and squirrels and, I guess, anything "wild" began ...

◆◆◆

Many years have gone by since those surreptitious trips to the park and during the ensuing years I have had more than my share of memorable wild-friends of all shapes and sizes. And, I've learned that when you invite wildlife into your garden, each season of each year brings exciting new friends and marvelous new experiences.

My first garden was a tiny one in North Bellmore. The 1960's were the years of DDT and every gardener I knew freely used chemicals, many times doubling up on the doses. Whenever I sprayed I felt awful and many years later, I learned why. Eventually, I stopped spraying, felt better, read anything that I could get my hands on about natural gardening – and in those days there wasn't much around – and began to "cultivate" my own style of gardening.

◆◆◆

In the 1990's, I moved farther east to Bay Shore and into a wonderful, white one-hundred-year-old Dutch colonial, replete with black shutters and a gambrel roof. My home overlooked Penataquit Creek, a small brackish-water creek that flowed into the Great South Bay and was part of Long Island's magnificent ecosystem of protected tidal wetlands. The Indians had named the creek Panothicut or Penataquit, which meant "crooked creek."

Summer alongside the creek was pure heaven for me - a perpetual vacation with warm weather and cooling ocean breezes. Surprisingly, the winter was also delightful. When the bay froze, the creek didn't - at least the part by my house and north - so all species of migrating ducks came to feed. I even had a pair of beautiful great blue herons visit on a regular basis and I especially loved watching them in the early dawn as they enjoyed fresh eels from the shallow waters of the creek!

The visiting ducks were avid bug hunters and kept my Bay Shore garden relatively pest-free. And, as an added benefit, my plants grew in leaps and bounds from all of their droppings. It was in this creek-front garden in western Suffolk County that I learned first-hand about "beneficials" and the balance of nature.

◆◆◆

In 2003, I moved eastward again, finally fulfilling my life-long dream of living in a small town. I'd found my "dream community" in a sleepy little hamlet on the East End of Long Island. Covenants and Restrictions were in place in my new community and natural conservation buffers, twenty-five and fifty feet deep surrounded each home, not only protecting the natural beauty of the land but also ensuring that there would be food and shelter for all native wildlife. I was thrilled to be part of a cutting-edge community that cherished the bounty of the land and the opulence of its wildlife.

◆◆◆

Year after year, I enriched the sandy soil with compost. I used no fertilizers and no chemicals. I planted trees and shrubs in the spots that made them happiest and I reaped the rewards of a well-balanced mini-ecosystem. The beneficials thrived in a chemically-free environment and took care of all the "bad guys." All I had to do was sit back and enjoy!

And, so it seems, for reasons I can't quite explain, this child of the city … of cement streets and gardenless homes … has always had a profound love for Mother Earth … in all her magnificence … in all her seasons …

◆◆◆

Each spring I am filled with a deep reverence as, once again, my garden awakens and becomes a garden of miracles … a place of rebirth and renewal. Spring is the season when my soul takes flight and my heart sings in excited anticipation of the bounty to come!

Nothing compares to the lushness of my summer garden, the fragrances of oriental lilies and roses, the early morning dew on the grass, the sweet tastes of vine-ripened heirloom tomatoes and freshly-picked raspberries and the gentle warmth that emanates from the soil.

The vivid oranges, yellows and browns of a fall woodland strike a chord deep in my soul but, as I watch the falling leaves, I am overcome with a sense of sadness as I think of the long, dark days ahead.

◆◆◆

In winter, there is a stark beauty to my garden … the outlines of trees and shrubs against a gray winter sky… the yellow and red twigs of dogwood … the black bark of my Kentucky coffee tree ... the infloresences of my miscanthus grasses gracefully bending under the weight of the falling snow ... and the dark rudbeckia seed-heads blowing in the chill winter winds.

So, I suppose, it seems rather fitting that my musings are not just about the pleasures of gardening or the joys of wildlife or the rewards of having a "mini" balanced ecosystem, but, rather, they are stories of one woman's attempts to successfully combine all three ... and, in so doing, I have found there is an abundance of unique stories that I would love to share with you about some of the extraordinary wild creatures who have visited my gardens ... who have stolen my heart ... and who have become my very special "wild-friends" ...

Chapter One

Summer's Gift...

Penataquit Creek, the meandering, thrice-forking creek that bordered my home in Bay Shore was approximately sixty feet across. Farther south it widened and became more beautiful with lovely old homes dotting both sides of the shoreline.

The creek was never quiet. It was always so alive with the quackings and honkings of its residents - many varieties of native and migrating ducks, Canada geese, swans, herons, egrets, coots and even a family of muskrats. Across the creek and opposite my home was a dredging company, replete with tug boats, barges, cranes, pipes and all manner of rusty equipment.

The dredging company had probably been there for a hundred years and, to most, it was a big messy jumble but, to me, it had a certain panache, a rather quaint charm, evoking a long-ago waterfront way of life. Definitely, as I've been told by my friends, a case of beauty being in the eye of the beholder!

◆◆◆

Looking back, the time I spent on Penataquit Creek was a wonderful interlude in my life, filled with very special treasured memories ...

There was the exciting summer when all of my wild Muscovy ducks were young and healthy and in full swing, so to speak. Over two hundred ducklings were born that year. There were so many new families that it was hard for me to tell them apart.

7

The lawn was overflowing with bright yellow and yellow-and-black ducklings of all sizes, shapes and personalities, from tiny little golf balls to gawky teenagers - all running around after the same bugs, all digging up the same worms and all falling on their heads as they frolicked in the grass which, at times, was taller than they were. The endearing little ducklings bickered with each other and gave their mothers migraines as they frantically tried to keep their children together in proper family groups.

◆◆◆

Next came the summer of the squirrels, when for some unbeknownst reason, my squirrels were extra plentiful and extremely friendly. It was the year that I began to buy peanuts, sunflower seeds and cracked corn in fifty-pound bags so I could keep their always empty munch-boxes filled. It was the summer I truly smiled for their breathtaking aerial acrobatics were simply spectacular.

That was followed by the summer of the swans. Sara Beth and Diablo took over my sanctuary behind the garage, raised their cygnets and devoured my newly planted Spartina spartinae (Coastal Cordgrass), Chasmanthium Latifolium (Northern Sea Oats) and Lysimachia clethroides (Gooseneck Loosestrife) all of which were supposed to have been the beginnings of my very own personal wetlands. The sweet little swan family ate tons of cracked corn and, in general, wreaked havoc in my sanctuary while thoroughly delighting everyone who saw them.

The adorable little cygnets grew from little gray fluffs into awkward teenagers, almost as big as their parents. It was such a thrill to watch their different personalities emerge. Just like us, some were shy, others brash and some so mischievous that Sara Beth and Diablo were always snuffle-snorting at them. On occasion, the harried parents even left them with me while they went off on a much needed vacation!

But, over the years, I have sadly and very painfully learned that nature gives and nature takes away and the summer of 2002 proved to be no exception. For some unknown reason, my swans and their babies returned only sporadically, my squirrel population had decreased drastically over the past two years, and I had sadly said my goodbyes to several of my special Muscovy ducks.

So, on a beautiful warm late June evening - the 20th to be exact, which is my son Michael's birthday - as I was about to enjoy a wonderful pasta dinner made with my sauce from the previous summer's tomato harvest, I heard strange screaming. I'd never heard these shrieking sounds before, and, try as I might, I couldn't imagine who was making such a ruckus.

◆◆◆

The next night and the one after that, just about dusk, the screaming grew even louder and more frantic, if that was at all possible. I was determined to get to the bottom of it. I looked all over to try to find the source, to no avail. I just never thought of looking in the dredging company complex across the creek.

By nature, I am a very early riser. I don't need an alarm clock since I always awaken with the sun. I love the peace and quiet of early morning and I find a special joy in the soothing sounds of the birds. It's one of the most special times of the day for me.

But on this particular Sunday, I was awakened before dawn by the same strange loud cries that I had heard at dusk the night before. My peace and serenity were totally disrupted by this unusual screeching and, needless-to-say, my curiosity was really aroused.

◆◆◆

Around eight, my bell rang and when I answered the door, I was surprised to see my neighbor Eric, a retired professor, avid sportsman and nature buff. "Did you see them? They're making a nest in the crane! You can really see them close-up from my backyard!"

I looked out my French doors and, sure enough, across the creek and forty feet above the ground on top of the huge crane that belonged to the dredging company was a pair of magnificent ospreys leisurely going about building their nest.

It seemed that my gift for that summer had just arrived ...

In awe, I watched as these majestic birds, second only to eagles, soared and glided and flapped their powerful wings as they worked diligently to build their mansion in the sky. Talk about a penthouse with a water view ... the Great South Bay and the Atlantic Ocean to the south and the Long Island Sound to the north!

I was utterly and completely fascinated. The male brought large three and four-foot long branches held securely in his strong feet and then tried to land atop the crane. What spectacular aerodynamics! Mesmerized, I couldn't stop watching.

Mrs. Osprey, of course, sat contentedly on her nest and, while not actually helping with the placement of whatever branches didn't fall to the ground, sort of screeched "helpful" comments to her husband. As for the branches, it was a win one, lose two or three situation. But, the nest did keep growing, albeit very slowly.

◆◆◆

Later on in the morning, the ospreys left and I called Betty, a wildlife rehabilitator I greatly respected, who was active in the Great South Bay chapter of the Audubon Society. She gave me several names and phone numbers and soon I was speaking with Jack, the president of the local chapter.

Jack came over early that afternoon, binoculars around his neck, and confirmed for me that a pair of ospreys was, indeed, building a nest on top of the crane. He explained that since ospreys usually build their nests in early spring, these were probably juveniles who were "checking out the neighborhood for next year." He also told me that it would probably be best if the ospreys laid no eggs since the babies most likely wouldn't have enough time to grow up.

Jack told me to call the New York State Department of Environmental Conservation first thing on Monday morning to ask their advice, which I did. I spoke to Dave, a marine biologist who was as excited as I was about my new family. However, this not being his field of expertise, he promised to call back as soon as he spoke to the proper agents.

True to his word, Dave called right back informing me that since ospreys are federally protected birds, I had to call the U. S. Department of Fish and Wildlife in Massachusetts where I learned that while ospreys are federally protected, they are no longer endangered which evidently makes a very big difference: As long

11

as there were no eggs in the nest, the osprey nest could be disturbed again and again in order to discourage them from building atop the crane. However, once the eggs were laid, the nest could not be touched until the young ospreys fledged.

◆◆◆

For a week, I faithfully watched before dawn each morning and again at dusk as the diurnal ospreys screamed and flew and built their nest. It was too much to hope that the workers at the dredging company wouldn't notice their new tenants since, more than likely, there was a huge pile of branches and debris at the base of the crane. And, I suspected that losing the use of their crane would be a hardship on my hard-working neighbors across the creek.

Sadly, right before the weekend, the workers fired up the old crane, lowered it and cleaned out the nest. Surprisingly, it took them quite a while. They left the crane in a lowered position, but they didn't bother to lower a big yellow companion crane. Over the weekend, the ospreys decided that perhaps they might also enjoy a yellow guest cottage and they immediately started construction on their second home.

◆◆◆

On Monday, the old crane went back up and the ospreys went back to building their dream house. Every night, the guys at the dredging company lowered the crane, took the nest down and then raised the crane back up. The minute they left, the ospreys once again began to rebuild. Finally, just before the July 4th weekend, which was an exceptionally long one that year, they lowered the crane one more time, cleaned out the nest and wove hot pink plastic ribbons around the crane and through all of its many mechanisms. They even placed a jaunty hot pink flag atop that fluttered almost patriotically in the warm ocean breezes. Well, the ospreys, far from being afraid of it, loved it. Over the four-day weekend, they worked feverishly constructing their "pink" mansion in the sky.

I watched in fascination as the male osprey which, incidentally, is the smaller of the birds, flew right over my home and, while in flight and without missing a wing beat, pulled dead branches from my trees with his extremely powerful feet. I also watched as he unsuccessfully tried to rip off a live branch from my zelkova tree and, seeing it limply hang, I realized that ospreys had been here last summer too!

Now the trick for Mr. Osprey was to land with a four-foot branch between his feet, on a nest that was on top of a forty-foot-high crane. His wings flapped furiously as he made many aborted attempts at landing until he was finally able to put the branch down on the nest. I held my breath, especially since most of the branches dropped to the ground.

◆◆◆

One morning, the male flew back from the bay with a big silver fish between his talons. The female was screaming for some but he nonchalantly went on the nearby utility pole enjoying it all by himself. It was very evident that he must be a juvenile since he certainly had a lot to learn about sharing with, caring for and pleasing his wife!

◆◆◆

By the end of the July 4th weekend, the nest was about four or five feet wide and looked fairly deep. The ospreys were delighted with the hot pink ribbons and I thought that they had decorated their home rather artistically. However, it didn't take long for me to realize that ospreys are not the greatest of nest builders. Their nest looked like a pile of branches carelessly thrown on top of each other. Whenever, one or the other would land, a part of the nest fell down. Being such a careful mother myself, it seemed to me a rather precarious place to raise babies and I silently wondered how many of their eggs would become osprey omelets!

The workers at the dredging company left the nest up until the following Friday and I secretly suspected that they were also excited by the ospreys. When they finally did lower the crane, it took them over a half-hour to dismantle the nest. They left the black crane lowered for the weekend and, once again, the ospreys worked on the yellow crane. No matter how many times their mansion and guest cottage were destroyed, the tenacious ospreys kept on rebuilding. There was simply no discouraging this energetic pair.

Not knowing that much about ospreys, I went online to do some research and what I learned only fascinated me more.

Ospreys, or fish hawks, as they are also known, are fairly large birds of prey approximately two-feet tall with a wing span of between four to six feet. They feed exclusively on live fish and fly thirty to one hundred feet above the surface of the water searching for their dinner with what can only be described as a phenomenal pair of eyes. Once they sight their prey, they hover with their wings beating and their legs trailing underneath their body, while they fine-tune their calculations before making their final dive.

Sometimes, they plunge straight into the water and, at other times, they make several readjustments before the final plunge. When ospreys make their final dive, their feet and head project ahead while their wings are held tight and high above their back. They make a spectacular dive, striking the water with a tremendous splash and sometimes disappearing momentarily below the surface, almost completely submerged, with only their wingtips showing.

Ospreys rise from the water dripping wet and gripping the twisting, slippery fish in their sharp talons. They then pause in mid-air to shake the water from their plumage and to rearrange the fish so that its head points forward thus reducing the fish's resistance to air and thereby making flying easier. The pads or lower surface of their toes are covered with spicules, which help them hold onto the slippery fish. Additionally, as with owls, the ospreys' outer toe is reversible thereby enabling them to grasp their prey more securely with two toes in front and two in the back.

Osprey plumage is compact, not feathery like an egret, which helps blunt the impact of diving into the water at top speed and also reduces the amount of water retained. What truly incredible, remarkable fisher-birds!

Ospreys arrive here on Long Island during March and April and, generally, use the same nest year after year. The nest can become quite large since more material is added prior to each nesting season. Ospreys three years or older usually mate for life.

Spring courtship marks the beginning of a five month period when the pair works together in perfect harmony to raise their young. The babies fledge at about eight weeks of age, and then remain in the area of the nest for about two months. In late August, the babies leave for their four-thousand-mile flight to South America with nothing but their internal compass to guide them. Once safely in South America, the youngsters stay there for two years and then return to their exact place of birth to begin the centuries old ritual of mating and raising their young. Utterly amazing!

◆◆◆

Here on the Island ospreys nest mostly in high dead trees and the many nesting platforms put up by the Long Island Power Authority (LIPA). Fortunately, for us, as long as they are not bothered, ospreys will nest close to people.

I always enjoyed sitting on my terrace in Bay Shore, delighting in the beauty of my garden and the antics of my wild-friends. But, that special summer, my eyes went ever upward, above the crest of the trees east of my home, constantly listening for the sound of their powerful wings as they beat a steady rhythm in the sky and waiting to see the incredible sea eagles return. I couldn't help but hold my breath for the ospreys in flight are truly majestic! There was so much beauty in Penataquit Creek but nothing compared to the splendor of this magnificent pair of raptors. Their grandeur was unsurpassed.

I felt so privileged that year to have shared in such an extraordinary gift of nature and I will always remember the exhilaration I felt as I watched a very special pair of young ospreys soar high into the warm summer sky...

Chapter Two

A Special Place in my Heart ...

He came into my life one late October day via my friend, Bridget, a north shore veterinarian who specialized in wildlife. A terrible storm had wreaked havoc on Long Island and Bridget asked if I would be able to raise a pair of non-related baby squirrels who had fallen out of their respective north and south shore tree nests. They were both healthy, approximately the same age, and needed a place that would afford them a little more growing-up time.

There was a slight catch though - by the time these baby squirrels would be old enough to be released it would be the middle of winter, certainly not a very friendly or hospitable time for two teenage squirrels to make their debut into "squirrel society" ... especially these two who didn't know anything at all about surviving in the outside world. Of course, it meant that I would have to keep them in my house throughout the winter and early spring since it would be late spring before they could safely be released into the wild.

Their "nursery" was in my workroom on the third floor of my home and their crib was a small pet carrier that I filled with fluffy towels. Like all babies, they either slept or ate, hungrily guzzling every drop of the special formula that I fed to them with tiny doll-like bottles. They made little grunting, growling noises, clung to my hands and scratched me with their sharp

17

little nails. Then, when they were satisfied, it was underneath the towels for a little nap, only to repeat the same routine two hours later.

When my "guests" outgrew their nursery, I moved them to my basement into a new high-rise apartment that was really a cat condo. Bridget had sent it to me with instructions to secure a large cardboard box at the top and to place a box of tissues on the bottom. I followed her instructions and watched in total fascination as my tenants very gently pulled one tissue at a time out of the box and then climbed up the sides of their multi-level home with one sheet of Kleenex in their little mouths. When they reached their new home, they vigorously shredded the tissue and then very carefully lined their nest.

◆◆◆

Pretty soon, as most new homeowners do, they began to remodel their home. At first, they added a new door, then some windows and finally a skylight that got pretty big until they were almost living totally outside. By then they needed a new house, so I found another cardboard box and, once again, after they felt comfortable, they proceeded to do the exact same thing. After renovating several cardboard homes, I felt the time had finally come for me to buy them a wooden structure … the harder to chew on with those sharp baby teeth … that was, in reality, a nesting box for large parrots.

Watching them grow and thrive was fascinating. They didn't have a mother to teach them and yet they instinctively knew how to do so many things, including burying their nuts underneath all the shredded tissues.

I purposely did not name them and I resisted the very strong temptation to cuddle them. I always want my wild-friends to be just that – wild and free – so, difficult as it was for me, I was very careful not to make them my pets.

◆◆◆

Finally, winter was gone, my tulips were in full bloom, and it was time to let the little guys out in the bright spring sunshine. Bridget had already sent me an outdoor release cage that she had had specially built for them. I placed a brand new wooden nest box at the top and I furnished their new home with all different kinds and sizes of tree branches so that they could hone up on their climbing skills.

They stayed inside their release cage for two weeks, busily climbing up and down the branches, sometimes falling on their heads and at other times making what I considered amazing jumps. The other squirrels and, of course, my ducks and geese came to visit every day watching, with amazement, the antics of these two clumsy critters. Everyone - human and "non" - was very interested in who was inside this strange looking contraption. But, mostly, I think, we all enjoyed watching the little guys simply learning to be what they were - wild squirrels.

◆◆◆

Finally, the big day came. The day every mother waits for and dreads, all at the same time. I felt the same anxiety that I had felt all those years ago when my three little boys had started school.

There were so many questions that raced through my mind. Will they know enough to stay away from predators? Will they know what to eat? Did I do these two a service or a disservice? Will they survive in the wild? How will they fare with my wild squirrels? After all, my gray babies didn't have a squirrel mom to teach them the ropes.

Well, apparently all my questions were moot. Neither of them wanted to leave the safety of their release cage. I left the door ajar and quietly went away, hiding just far enough away so that I could see them but they couldn't see me. But they still both refused to leave.

Some of my friends encouraged me to give them the boot quickly but I wanted them to slowly adjust to their new surroundings without any unnecessary trauma. Every day I watched as they happily played and frolicked inside the open cage. Finally after about a week, they both ventured outside, but only a foot or two from the cage, and then they ran right back in. I guess just like human babies, they needed their "security blanket!"

Well, so far, this was definitely not going as I had planned, but then I kept reminding myself that "whenever you deal with Mother Nature nothing ever goes as planned!"

Three weeks had now gone by and, at last, my young squirrels were exploring the large trees outside of their cage, but they made so much noise as they haphazardly crashed through the branches that I was sure every predator on Long Island would hear them and come after them. Gradually though they finally began to enlarge their perimeters. However, each and every night they came back to their "home." That meant that each and every night, in the dark, I had to walk down my long driveway and go behind my garage into my sanctuary to make sure that they were safely ensconced in their nest box. Then I had to shut and lock the release cage door lest some predator attack them inside the cage. This was no easy feat since they had no curfew and when they were cuddled inside their nest box, it was usually so dark that I couldn't see them. I had to listen for their little annoyed grumps and growls.

As my little friends expanded their territory, I watched with amusement and some amount of trepidation as they constantly returned to my house. For some reason, they liked climbing up and peering into my windows and it always brought a big smile to my face whenever I happened to walk into my living room and saw their happy little faces intently staring in. I just hoped that they weren't trying to return to their comfy home in the basement. For obvious reasons, I decided not to mention this little aspect of their development to anyone.

Finally, the teenagers became real squirrels, happily romping all over the yard, silently climbing trees, no longer falling on their heads, no longer crashing through the branches.

Suddenly, I noticed that all my wild squirrels had very mysteriously vanished. I tried to tell my little guys that this was not appropriate behavior. Didn't I buy their peanuts, corn and sunflower seeds in fifty-pound bags? Wasn't there always enough food to go around? Did they really have to chase everyone away? I didn't raise bullies, did I? Where were their manners!

Eventually, one of the squirrels went his own way, but the other stayed in the big trees that bordered my garden. Every time, I went out back, he miraculously appeared out of nowhere following me around all day, tugging on my jeans for his peanuts. If I didn't respond immediately, he thought nothing of climbing up my leg, going into my pocket and helping himself to a peanut. I named him "Fatso" because he ate so many peanuts that he actually had little roles of fat, something quite unusual for my agile little friends.

Of course, I could never leave my house without peanuts in my pockets. In fact, whenever I went into my garden, I had the distinct feeling that mischievous brown eyes were constantly watching my every move. Sure enough, within minutes, my little gray friend would appear, begging, so pathetically, with his hand over his heart.

◆◆◆

As the weather grew colder, I began to wear a light sweatshirt jacket ... of course, one with squirrels on it ... and Fatso quickly ascertained that I now kept his peanuts in the jacket pocket and, if I dared to take it off, he'd find it no matter where and just reach into the pockets and help himself. He even made himself an old-fashioned pocket-door entrance!

Whenever I took Gypsy, my blue merle collie, for a walk to the ferries, Fatso would follow overhead on the utility wires. On one of these walks, a friend of mine refused to believe that the squirrel tagging along and doing daredevil tricks on the high-wire above was indeed Fatso. All I had to do was put my hand in my pocket and, lo and behold, much to the chagrin of my friend - the original "doubting Thomas" - down raced my furry little fat friend for his treat.

Fatso and I spent many wonderful late summer afternoons sitting on my stone garden bench, talking and simply enjoying each other's company. He ate so many peanuts that, at times, I could almost swear he had a green tinge. I knew that he was storing up fat for the winter but at the rate he was going, he wouldn't have to leave his winter's nest until springtime!

◆◆◆

For almost three years, I enjoyed the pleasure of Fatso's company and when, one warm spring day, he came no more, I felt as if I'd lost my best friend … but, as my tears silently fell, they were softened by the beautiful memories of the very special bond I shared with my little gray "wild-friend."

Chapter Three

Another Time ...
Another Place ...

Once again, Penataquit Creek is quiet. New bright green leaves whisper softly as mild ocean breezes set them aflutter. All of the comings and goings, the raucous honkings and quackings of early spring are now just fond memories ... put aside in my mind ... for me to call up later on ... whenever my heart needs a respite from the harsh icy winds of winter.

The many mallards who had graced my snow-covered lawn all winter and, then, somewhat abruptly, left for parts and places unknown, have now returned to the creek as they do each spring, with their tiny ducklings in tow.

Father Goose no longer sits on my dock watching over Mother Goose as she nests across the creek. They are much too busy taking care of their energetic, inquisitive and hungry long-legged goslings.

As much as I enjoy everyone who flies, runs or hops into my creek-front garden, the highlight of my day always comes when my old friends, Diablo and his love, Sara Beth, return.

Perhaps, they are so very special to me simply because they are such a challenge. Adult swans are extremely independent - almost haughty, at times - and none more so than Diablo. The older he gets, the more imperious Diablo becomes.

Whenever Diablo is hungry, he swims into an area of the creek that I can see from my French doors and sticks his long neck over the dock, as if it were a periscope. Then he stares with an extremely demanding glare that lets me know in no uncertain terms that he is here and hungry. Even though it is about one-hundred-fifty-feet from my kitchen to the dock, I always feel that Diablo is looking right at me.

I know that I spoil him because I always drop whatever it is that I am doing and run right down to feed him. And, thus, he's taught me to be at my duck ramp between five and six o'clock because that's the time when he brings Sara Beth for dinner. And, if I should dare to be engrossed in something or other and not realize he is waiting for me, my beautiful "devil" wreaks such havoc in the creek with the geese that their extremely loud honking and wild splashing always alert me to his presence.

◆◆◆

When I first moved to Bay Shore, I watched in awe as a very young Sara Beth and Diablo glided effortlessly along the surface of the water, barely making a ripple. Their feathers, so pure and white, glistened in the early morning sun and glowed under the soft moonlight. At the time, I couldn't imagine a more beautiful or serene sight, but, as I got to know them, reality set in rather quickly for Diablo was anything but serene!

◆◆◆

My first encounters with Diablo were a little on the scary side and I was filled with dread every time I had to climb aboard my boat. Finally, I began luring Diablo away with food so I could hurry on or off.

Diablo treated Sara Beth just as shabbily! He bit her. He chased her. He constantly bullied her. It was no wonder that Sara Beth was terrified of him too.

◆◆◆

Then one day, Sara Beth disappeared. The first few days Diablo didn't seem to miss her at all. But, as the days turned into weeks, he became very melancholy. He refused to eat. He came to me for sympathy and each day, as I sat on the dock gently talking to him, I tried coaxing him to eat. Nothing worked. I do believe that Diablo sensed how much I cared and, I think, it was then, during those lonely weeks, that our special friendship began.

Ever the romantic, I was certain that Diablo was going to die of a broken heart. I called my friend Bridget who is a wildlife veterinarian for some advice and I learned that it's not unusual for an "abused" female swan to leave her mate. I sometimes wonder if this was really true or if it was simply Bridget being very kind knowing it was something I would like to hear.

◆◆◆

Weeks turned into a month, then almost two, and still no sign of Sara Beth. Diablo was inconsolable. It broke my heart to see this big, aggressive swan so sad.

Then, out of the blue, Sara Beth returned. At first, she seemed hesitant around Diablo, a little wary, almost waiting for Diablo to bite her. But, to his credit, he didn't. He seemed to have missed Sara Beth immensely.

Once again, it gave me great pleasure to watch them eat at my duck ramp, upending, completely at ease with each other, knowing all was right in their world. Unbelievably, Sara Beth had transformed Diablo into "her kind of swan" - attentive, caring and non-violent! I guess in her ladylike way, she taught him a lesson he wouldn't soon forget. In fact, I've yet to see him behave in any other than a gentlemanly manner with Sara Beth … and even with me!

It's another story, however, with the Canadian geese. Each spring as Sara Beth begins her search for a nesting site, Diablo refuses to allow the geese to swim in the water. He spends literally hours patrolling the creek with his beautiful wings raised in attack mode. The geese have also nested alongside the creek for years, so they know exactly how to stay out of his way. Still, Diablo swimming at top speed and in full armament is truly a sight to behold!

◆◆◆

As Sara Beth and Diablo came to trust me more, they allowed me wonderful glimpses into their private lives. One special day, I was privileged to witness their courtship ritual. I cannot adequately describe the beauty and delicacy of their movements, their long graceful necks dipping into the creek, splashing water, first one, then the other, then both, until they ultimately tenderly placed their faces together, arching their necks, forming an actual heart. Truly a sight I shall never forget.

◆◆◆

Each Mothers' Day, I carefully watch for Sara Beth. When I see her wings upraised and rounded I

27

know there will be little gray heads sticking out from between them. I love to see her as she gently lowers her body so the cygnets can scramble down into the water. And, yes, sometimes, even she has a baby who holds on for dear life, not wanting to leave the safety of his mommy!

Like all new parents, Sara Beth and Diablo are extremely proud of their cygnets and, each year, as I exclaim over their new little family, Diablo gets up high in the water, puffs up his wings and makes a sort of "job well done" type of snort-snuffle. He always makes me laugh for I truly believe that he likes to be complimented!

◆◆◆

Once the babies are all in the water, Sara Beth begins to daintily churn up the bottom of the creek with her webbed feet allowing all the "goodies" to float to the surface so that her babies can dine on the creek's many delicacies. I enjoy watching as she gently teaches them to eat the cracked corn I throw on the duck ramp. At first, the cygnets prefer to eat the natural foods. However, after watching their mom nibble at the cracked corn, they slowly begin to taste it, then enjoy it and, finally, clumsily begin "up-ending" for some!

Much to my delight, Sara Beth and Diablo often bring their little family to dine at my waterfront restaurant. They are such superb parents, always allowing their cygnets to eat until they are satiated before they take their turn. And, then, one at a time, Sara Beth or Diablo have their dinner while the other guards their little family.

◆◆◆

A few summers back, one of their babies had fishing line wrapped all around him. He was so scared. He frantically swam all over the creek as an equally frantic Sara Beth swam after him. Of course, the more he swam, the tighter the fishing line became. I was horrified. I called to the swans to come to my duck ramp - "Swans, bring your baby to me, I'll help him" - hoping all the time that none of my neighbors heard. I was sure they would have me committed!

I could not believe my eyes when Sara Beth and Diablo began pushing their baby to me and then guided him up my duck ramp. I had my trusty fishing net with me and I very slowly caught the cygnet and pulled him up. Sara Beth and Diablo were on either side of the ramp intently watching me. I waited for them to hiss at me, a sure sign that they were upset, but, they seemed relatively calm - much calmer, in fact, than I was!

Once their baby was on the dock, I lifted off a portion of my fish net and was able, fortunately, to unravel the fishing line, cut it all off and put him back in the creek. When I was done, Sara Beth and Diablo calmly walked up the ramp to eat their dinner. The baby, however, just glared at me from the safety of the creek. Ever since, whenever one of their babies is caught in fishing line, Sara Beth and Diablo bring him to the duck ramp and graciously allow me to help.

◆◆◆

As fall approaches, Sara Beth sometimes leaves her babies with Diablo while she takes some down time by herself. I usually find her in my sanctuary waiting for me. She likes the special treats that I bring her and, I think, she enjoys not having to share them with anyone. We have developed our own kind of communication. I pull some weeds and she follows me around, making those strange little swan sounds. It's been a long four months and Sara Beth seems exhausted.

It is now very important for Sara Beth to regain her strength because next comes the most physically taxing part for her and Diablo - the flying lessons. What an incredible sight to see! One parent, up front, shows the babies how to fly while the other parent comes from behind chasing them and forcing them "up, up and away." It takes a lot of prompting and nipping from the swan-parent who takes up the rear – who I assume is Diablo - before the babies get the idea and the courage to attempt to fly, but, when at last they do, what fun they have!

◆◆◆

By late October, the babies, still mostly gray, are almost full-grown. It's such a funny sight to watch them climb up the duck ramp. They remind me of "baby Godzillas" as they lumber up the duck ramp to the dock. They are still growing and voraciously devour bowls and bowls of food.

Even though the cygnets are almost as big as adult swans, they still have their baby personalities. They get along with everyone: me, the mallards and, especially, with Elizabeth, the young goose, who often joins them for dinner. They are still very innocent. They have yet to learn that they are not only the biggest birds in the creek, but also the most beautiful. They have not yet realized the fact that they are royalty.

With Sara Beth and her teenagers in my sanctuary, there is hardly room for me. Their routines have begun to change. Sara Beth no longer waits for her children to eat first. It's now a free-for-all at dinnertime, with Sara Beth and Diablo winning most of the time.

Sara Beth and Diablo also spend a lot of time apart, each taking their turns watching their offspring. Sometimes, they even manage to go off together for a few hours of peace and quiet, content in the knowledge that no predator would dare bother their "kids" now!

But, the babies still have their last and most important lesson to learn - they must become independent, able to cope in the wild without their parents' protection. And, Diablo and Sara Beth will now use every tool available to them to make certain that their babies will survive!

◆◆◆

In December the time comes for me to sadly begin saying my goodbyes to the babies. There are very few gray feathers left. They are almost all white and the day is fast approaching when, in nature's scheme of things, they must be on their own. Sara Beth and Diablo will soon see to it that their children "leave the nest."

For me, it is very bittersweet. I have taken great pleasure in watching them grow so big in such a relatively short period of time. I have laughed at their silly antics and cried when one of them didn't return home. I have come to love them. They have become my dear little friends.

And, now, they must follow their instincts. They must court and mate and raise families. They must follow the ways of the wild. And, I will tell myself that this is nature's way ... that Sara Beth and Diablo must prepare for next year's babies ... that I will, once again, have so very much to look forward to in the spring ... but first ... I must wipe away my tears ...

Chapter Four

The $227.00 Duckling ...

I always found one each spring - an abandoned little duckling that had hatched long after his mother and his siblings had left their nest. No matter how often it happened, this amazing miracle of life always filled me with a sense of wonder. And even though I knew the odds were truly stacked against me, I always brought the tiny duckling into my home ... and into my heart ... cleaned the little guy up and prayed that he or she would make it this time. Sadly, they almost never did.

The ducklings usually survived for only a week or two. By then, of course, I had fallen in love with them and the loss was devastating. I have to believe that in most cases Mother Nature did know best and that the little ducklings were either too weak or too sick to survive in the wild. But, that being said, I could never just leave them there to die, cold and alone. So, I helped them, as best I could, and hoped that one day maybe - just maybe - I would finally meet a little duckling who would beat the odds...

This time, it started one stormy night in April of 2000, in a utility area that housed my air conditioning units and my garbage pails. It was surrounded on two sides by my house and a second story sun porch and on the other two sides by large cedar planters of varying heights, all of which made a cozy little nesting place for the ducks, full of warm sunshine and inviting nooks and crannies.

Evidently, during the storm, one of the garbage pails had blown against the house, leaning on it at a rather precarious angle, and leaving just enough room the next day for Hope, one of my Muscovy ducks, to sneak underneath. Clearly, Hope felt that it was an absolutely perfect site for her spring nest and that is where, a few days later, I found her happily sitting on the warm pebbles, hollowing out a spot for her eggs. When she was not sitting on her nest, I'd look up to find her perched atop the lattice railing of my second-story sun porch guarding her chosen spot from all intruders.

◆◆◆

Two weeks went by and every day I saw another egg in the nest that Hope had so very carefully built underneath the shelter of the pail. Ever grandma duck, I braced the pail up against the house with one of my most expensive clay flowerpots, hoping that the weight of the flowerpot would hold the pail in place so that it wouldn't fall on Hope or, when she wasn't there, her eggs.

As she laid more and more eggs, Hope began to concentrate, as any mother-to-be would, on making her nest secure. And to keep her eggs hidden and at the proper temperature, she carefully covered her eggs whenever she left with lots of fluffy white down.

Amazingly, Hope had the most attentive husband. Unlike most Muscovy males, he patiently stayed within calling distance. As Hope began to spend more and more time on her nest, he too spent more and more time waiting for her and watching over her. In all my years of taking care of Muscovy ducks, I have never seen a male stay by the nest for such a long time.

Then, much to my surprise, he began to sit on the nest every time Hope decided that she needed a break. Whenever she left to eat or bathe or just stretch her legs, Papa took over. My instincts told me that this was going to be a most unusual event!

Just before Hope's eggs were due to hatch, I discovered that I had no hot water in the house. I tried everything but could not find the problem. Finally, I called the local plumber who discovered that the pail shading Hope's nest was also blocking my hot water heater vent and, in fact, had melted onto the vent covering it completely. Imagine the plumber's face when I told him he'd have to work over Hope's nest and to "please be extremely careful of my expectant mother." My bill, a little padded, I suppose, due to the unusual working conditions and the extra stress experienced by the plumber: $227.00!

◆◆◆

On June 20th, the day that I underwent joint replacement surgery in my left hand, I groggily came home to the wonderful, uplifting sight of Hope parading her five beautiful little yellow ducklings all over the lawn. I delightedly watched as she introduced her adorable fluffy yellow "golf balls" to my garden. She took them for a leisurely stroll along the perimeters of the property and then, into my "courtyard," where they all had a quick nap cuddled underneath Mama.

When the ducklings awakened, Hope marched them underneath the cedar deck into an adjacent area known as my bird sanctuary since it's always filled with wonderful songbirds. It is a true wildlife habitat, heavily planted with shrubs to nest in, many kinds of berry-producing shrubs to dine on, lots of bird baths and all sorts of special goodies for my little feathered friends.

◆◆◆

When Hope arrived in the bird sanctuary, her older sister Marguerite was already there with her brood. You can just imagine the utter chaos as all the ducklings ran around while their mothers frantically tried to sort out who belonged to whom!

Finally, peace and quiet reigned and everyone happily munched, sat or swam in the bowls of cracked corn and water that I had quietly sneaked out for them.

◆◆◆

Two days later, as I looked for Hope and her babies, I passed by her now supposedly empty nest and heard a faint little peeping sound. When I went down the steps to look I saw a little yellow duckling laying in the hot sun, covered in mushy yolk from his egg and, most likely, from the other broken eggs too, looking for all the world like a scrambled egg omelet, and not knowing what to do except softly peep for help.

With my one good hand, I picked him up and quickly brought him into the house for a thorough cleaning. He seemed so helpless and so very vulnerable. I really didn't think he would survive the night. I put lots of cuddly towels in a little box to keep him toasty warm and hoped for the best. I didn't worry too much about feeding him that first day because I knew from past experience that for the first day or two of their lives, chicks usually never eat much. I think they get a great deal of nourishment from their egg yolk sac.

◆◆◆

The next day I made him a concoction I call "duck soup." No, it's not made from ducks or chickens, but from duck pellets which I mix with water and then mash until the whole thing becomes soupy. Well, the little guy just loved his duck soup. He couldn't get enough of it. He also couldn't get enough of me. I guess I was imprinted on him because he followed me around everywhere. And when he didn't see me, he just peeped louder and louder until I came and got him.

Peeper, as I fittingly called him, was now able to jump pretty high and the second night, even though I had covered the top of his "nest" box, he jumped out. In the morning, I found him calmly sitting by his food dish waiting for me to prepare his duck soup. The next night he graduated into my secure duck carrier where there was no escaping. I think Peeper was happy because he could see out of the mesh wire door and I was certainly happy because I had the security of knowing that he was protected when I wasn't there to look after him.

Peeper now had quite a regular routine. He either followed me around the house or he took naps with me or he ate. I'd never had a duckling that ate so well. I was really beginning to believe that this little yellow "fuzz-ball" would make it.

Peeper loved our naps together and they certainly aided in my recuperation. Every time I lay down, my little Peeper came to bed with me, snuggling under my hair. When we woke up and I wanted to transport him quickly, I just placed him in my sling. I'm not quite sure what the wonderful surgeon who repaired my hand would think of this innovative use of his sling though! Peeper, however, loved this new mode of transportation. It was like a little swing for him and for a time, he happily went everywhere with me, snuggled inside, sitting atop my cast.

◆◆◆

As the days flew by, he became quite frisky and continually tried to jump out of my sling, especially when he didn't want to go where I did. His next mode of transportation was my deep pocket. As he grew older he especially liked that ride, because he could see much better. He'd stick his little yellow head out and off we'd go.

After I had him a few weeks, I realized that unlike most of the other ducklings I had tried to raise, Peeper was actually thriving. I made several attempts to put him back with his mother and his three remaining siblings because I felt that this would be his best chance for survival. His mother always accepted him, but, Peeper wouldn't accept her. Each time I tried to leave, he ran back to me, peeping full blast, and wouldn't let me out of his sight. Of course, I unashamedly loved it!

When I did have to go out during the day, I'd leave Peeper in the kitchen. Like a good little duckling, he stayed underneath my cockatiel Happy Bird's cage and that was where I'd find him when I got home. As he got older, he learned the sound of the front door opening and knew that it meant that I'd come home and he'd race down the foyer to greet me, peeping as loudly as he could.

Peeper truly began to take over my household and whenever he heard the doorbell ring, he'd run to greet "his" guests. Peeper even began to learn my daily routine and in the morning, I'd find him ensconced underneath the kitchen table waiting for me to have my breakfast. After breakfast, he insisted on a play period. He loved to bite my sneakers or peck at my jeans. Peeper also loved to play tug-o-war and he usually won!

◆◆◆

As the weeks passed, I started to feel a little better and I found myself taking Peeper outside more often. We'd either sit in the shade of my pear trees or walk around my garden just as I'd seen the other mother ducks do. I introduced him to new things and enjoyed his reactions, but, as much as he enjoyed his new found freedom, he always ran back to me.

I also wanted to get him used to the other ducks and to supplementing my "duck soup" with the bugs and grasses that all little baby ducklings need for a healthy balanced diet. His instincts took over quickly and he was soon running around at top speed catching all sorts of yummy critters. At one point, a friend of mine dug up a worm for Peeper, but, while Peeper knew what to do with it, he didn't seem too thrilled with the taste!

◆◆◆

Outside, I had no fear of losing Peeper. He was my little shadow, following me everywhere. He was always underfoot and I had to be very careful not to step on him.

As Peeper spent more and more time running around outside, it was only a matter of time before the neighboring crow family discovered him. As they relentlessly circled overhead looking for a tasty tidbit for their lunch or dinner, I found myself constantly involved in major warfare with them. Whenever I saw their large black shadows on the ground, I'd look up and yell at them: "You're messin' with the wrong Mama this time... Don't even think about it!" But whenever Peeper was at play in the yard, I had to be extra vigilant.

By now, Hope had lost all of her ducklings, most likely to the crow family. It is always so sad for me to watch a Muscovy mother search for her missing family. Hope spent days endlessly looking for her babies, clucking softly under shrubs and flowers hoping they would hear her calls and come back.

Of her own accord, Hope came over several times to try to befriend Peeper. She wanted to teach him all sorts of things, but he wanted none of it. He always ran away from her and came to sit by me. I had to wonder if somehow Hope knew that Peeper was one of hers.

◆◆◆

Time flew and I could not believe that Peeper was already one month old. I suddenly began to realize that he had no idea that he was a duck. I truly believed that Peeper thought that he was just a small yellow person. Sadly, I knew the time had come for me to stop treating him like my little baby.

And so, much as I didn't want him to, Peeper spent his first day totally outside in his duck cage. It was time for him to learn that he was a duckling.

Muscovies are exceptionally friendly ducks and, whenever anyone is in the duck cage, they are always very interested and very social. Peeper had plenty of visitors but none as faithful as Lucky, the older Pekin duckling that I was also rehabilitating. During the day, whenever I was outside, I let Peeper out of his cage as much as possible and I could see that he was slowly on the road to becoming a real duckling. He had his favorite bushes and he knew his way around the yard. He always came back to me and I had no trouble putting him in his duck cage at night which I would then place in the garage so that no night critters would bother him.

As Peeper became less tame, Lucky tried relentlessly to befriend him. Of course, Lucky terrified Peeper. Lucky was so big and clumsy. I'm sure that to Peeper Lucky looked just like Godzilla. At first, Peeper ran away from these encounters but Lucky was persistent and followed at a fast clip right behind. I watched this go on for days until one day I noticed that they were sitting rather close and so began their special friendship.

It was heartwarming to see the big adolescent Pekin and the little yellow Muscovy duckling sitting underneath my hydrangeas and, while not quite sitting side by side, at least they were sitting within a foot or two of each other. I was so glad that Peeper had made an older friend - one who could show him the ropes which Lucky wholeheartedly did.

◆◆◆

The weeks went by and Peeper was almost two months old. He was getting harder and harder to put in his cage at night. It now took me quite a while to catch him. And then one night the inevitable that I so feared finally happened – Peeper ran so quickly into my wildlife sanctuary that I couldn't catch him.

I've purposely let the land behind my garage and adjacent to the creek become overgrown and wild because so many of the birds and ducks love this truly natural area. But, that night, it all worked against me. I couldn't even find Peeper. I looked for over an hour and then it began to storm. I was soaking wet and I knew I'd never find him that awful dark night. Heartbroken, I had to give up.

I didn't sleep well that night and I woke up very early the next morning, I looked all over for my little Peeper but he was nowhere to be found. I looked for Peeper for days to no avail.

Did he swim off in the creek? Will he come back some day? I knew what my head told me had probably happened, but my heart told me differently, and, I guess, for once, I just wanted to believe my heart.

I knew that I had been very lucky to have Peeper in my life - even for such a short time. His antics and his happy little personality eased both the physical pain of my surgery and the emotional pain from the recent loss of my beautiful blue merle collie, Gypsy Blue. Once again, there was someone waiting for me when I came home, someone to play with outside and someone to cuddle inside.

Maybe next year there'll be another little Peeper for me to help and maybe next year, I'll see that duckling grow up all the way. Sometimes, I find it's so very sad to love my wild friends ... and to want them to be free ... I cry a lot ...

Chapter Five

A Brief Moment
in Time ...

In 1993, when I moved into my new home in Bay Shore, the house sat in the middle of a very uncared for piece of land. Partly overgrown and partly sandy and weedy, very few of the original trees and shrubs were alive and the wildlife I so loved was virtually non-existent.

The house was actually quite stately – a traditional white Dutch colonial with black shutters. But its elegance was somewhat diminished because it was completely surrounded by perfectly-pruned-into-rectangles spreading yews that somehow reminded me of the landscaping currently in vogue at the local funeral homes!

There was a bright spot though ... I found a big old leggy lilac bush and an ancient, overgrown shrub rose both trying very hard, but rather unsuccessfully, to compete with the weeds and the "killer" oriental bittersweet vines. I immediately knew that one of my first projects would be to begin the years-long project of restoring them to their natural beauty.

I clipped and pruned, and, then, I pruned some more, and slowly, over the next few years, my lilac and rose began to look like the beautiful shrubs that they were meant to be. As with any plants that are cared for and loved, they rewarded me with an abundance of beautiful blossoms, marvelous fragrances and, in the fall, lots of rose hips for my birds to enjoy.

Throughout those early years, I planted and I researched and I worked very hard to create my own wildlife sanctuary. In fact, in 2001, the National Wildlife Federation accredited my "sanctuary" as a Certified Backyard Wildlife Habitat.

◆◆◆

That spring, I decided to add a great room to my home. Its wall of floor-to-ceiling windows would overlook the creek and my gardens, allowing me to really enjoy my wild visitors, especially during the cold winter months. So up came the multi-level deck and out came my Kousa dogwood and my stewardia tree and lots of shrubs and perennials, all lovingly dug out, put aside and mulched, ready to be replanted when all the construction was finished.

My songbirds and squirrels adjusted to their moved feeders with a minimum of fuss, as did the Canadian geese. The female Muscovy ducks that usually nested alongside my house good-naturedly looked elsewhere that year. Some of my male muscovies, however, were extremely upset with all the chaos of the new construction and one, in particular, wandered around in a daze. All my "homeless" duck needed was a shopping cart and a cardboard box!

But, no one was more upset than Misty Blue, my one-year-old blue merle collie. She definitely did not like any of the changes that were taking place in her yard and she wasn't too thrilled with the fact that her serene puppy existence had been totally disrupted by all of those big yellow, noisy machines.

◆◆◆

One day, completely out of the blue, Misty became fascinated with the bottom step of my cedar staircase. I just couldn't keep her away. I thought that one of the workers had spilled soda on the step and I kept hosing it down. But, every time that I succeeded in chasing her, she ran right back, constantly smelling and licking the step. Nothing I did seemed to work. No matter how many times I shooed her away, Misty stubbornly kept going back to the exact same spot.

◆◆◆

Finally, the next day, exasperated, I decided to have a closer look to see just exactly what it was that was so fascinating to my "little Mist." When I bent down to look more closely at the step, I couldn't believe my eyes. Underneath the planks of cedar in the opening between the boards, I saw something move.

At first I thought that one of my nesting ducks had become entrapped, but, then, I realized that I was looking at soft gray fur not dirty white feathers. And what I saw enchanted me ... several pairs of sleepy brown eyes curiously looking up at me ... It seemed a little opossum family had taken up residence. I could see the babies cuddling and climbing all over their mother. And, best of all, no one seemed to mind me watching!

44

I was so excited. I had never seen an opossum "nest" before. I wanted to watch the babies grow. I wanted to leave food for them. I wanted to make up to the little opossum family for my unwitting destruction of their habitat.

While eagerly beginning my mental preparations, I was suddenly shocked to discover that I really knew very little about opossums. I, of course, knew that opossums are marsupials and just like kangaroos and koalas, the infants stay inside their mothers' pouch to nurse and develop.

I also knew that they are primarily nocturnal, play dead when threatened, foraged in the uncovered garbage cans next door, weren't the cutest of my evening visitors … although, probably, precisely for that reason, I have always had a soft spot in my heart for them … and, finally, that my opossum mother most likely lived underneath my deck and, due to the construction, was probably recently dispossessed.

What I didn't know was that opossums shared their world with the dinosaurs and that their babies are so small when they are born that twenty can fit into one teaspoon, a discovery which made me realize that most of the members of my new little opossum family were already teenagers!

I also learned that, unlike my ducks who made a nest and then occupied it for two months while waiting for their eggs to hatch, opossums make no "nest" because they rarely stay in the same place for more than two or three days.

Furthermore, I didn't quite realize how beneficial opossums are to our environment. They love all types of bugs and insects. Snails and slugs are an absolute delicacy. Since they help keep our neighborhoods clean and free of unwanted, harmful garden pests and rodents, some of which might carry diseases, it's no wonder that, in the scientific world, opossums are known as "nature's little sanitation engineers." And, in addition to all of this, in the fall, they even clean up the rotting fruit that falls from our trees!

The more online research I did, the more captivated I became by my sweet little family. Late at night, whenever I took Misty outside, I constantly looked for them and, one dark night, I was rewarded by the remarkable and unforgettable sight of my little mother carrying her babies on her back. This is the time when she begins to teach them their basic survival skills such as how to find food and avoid predators.

I diligently began to listen for the little sounds opossums make and, sure enough, on another of my nightly forays, I could tell by their little clicks and sneezes that they were running around in my shrubs. Enthralled, I stood very still listening to their lively, animated conversations although not understanding one word of them.

And, so, from such a fleeting encounter, I found myself that summer looking each and every night for the cute little opossum family who blissfully inhabited my world for such a brief moment in time, hoping, just hoping, to catch one more glimpse …

Chapter Six

Peanut

Written with deep sadness and a great sense of loss on April 23, 2001 ...

This afternoon, I lost my best friend... my sweet little Peanut. My special girl flew her final flight, taking wing, so gracefully, across the Rainbow Bridge. I shall never forget her for, of all the ducks that I have ever loved, she was, and probably always will be, my favorite ...

I named her Peanut not because she was tiny but because she loved the peanuts that I always carried in my pocket for the squirrels. She relentlessly followed me, clucking and fussing, looking at me with her soulful brown eyes and pecking at my leg, until I had no recourse but to give her the peanuts that she so enjoyed.

And, of course, it wasn't enough to just give her a peanut. I had to slightly crush the shell and stay with her while she daintily nibbled up every morsel. If I tried to leave before she was finished eating, she loudly complained. She just hated it when the big Muscovy males tried to steal her peanuts. I suppose the peanuts were the building blocks that cemented our special friendship and, over time, she and I developed a extraordinary bond with our own unique means of communication.

Peanut was born almost eight summers ago. Her mother, Grace, made her nest in my favorite white

47

wrought iron planter. Since it was on my porch, I could check on Grace and I was fascinated as a new egg appeared almost daily.

And, when the big moment came, I felt extremely privileged to be allowed to watch the special event! One of Grace's eggs, though, had previously caught my attention since it was much bigger than the others. As I watched the shell begin to shatter, I was truly amazed to see the twins - Peanut and Patches - emerge from the cracked shell.

Peanut and Patches were almost identical and, for quite some time, I had trouble telling them apart. But, as they grew, their distinct personalities began to emerge making it much easier for me. It seemed to me that Peanut had the brains. And, according to the arduous male muscovies, Patches had inherited the beauty!

◆◆◆

For many years, Peanut was my dominant female Muscovy. She set the rules, argued with all the girls, won all the "discussions" and always picked the best nesting spots which were usually very close to my home and me so that I could give her the extra attention that she demanded and which, of course, she felt she deserved - the little bowls of water and corn that made nest-sitting go faster and easier, lots of fresh water for her bath and a straw broom nearby that I had no hesitancy using to discourage the overly amorous Muscovy males who constantly bothered her.

Peanut almost always won my "Mother of the Year" award. She was a strict mother and her little ducklings learned at a very early age that "mama knew best." And mama absolutely did!

Peanut fiercely protected her little ones from the crows and the seagulls and the raccoons and everyone and everything that she felt might harm them. It didn't take Peanut too long to figure out that her job of protecting her babies was made much easier when she allowed me to "help" her. Of course, I was very flattered and constantly told her so!

Whenever I gardened, Peanut would march over with her brood trailing close behind and ensconce herself and her little family in one of the shady spots in the garden. From underneath the flowers, she would cluck at the ducklings, giving them their orders which they always – always - unquestioningly obeyed!

She knew that no crow or seagull would dare bother her when she was with me and, should a duckling fall into the creek, well, of course, I would scoop it up in my fishing net. And, if the babies seemed hungry, "Grandma Duck" would stop whatever she was doing to prepare their duck soup.

Silly as it may seem to some, Peanut and I became friends and, as good friends often do, she apparently thought nothing of visiting me whenever the mood struck her. Sometimes I'd just find her sitting by my heavy wooden front door, patiently waiting, and other times she would peck rather loudly on my back French doors - a short duck's way of ringing the doorbell, I guess - to remind me that I was remiss in my "grandmotherly" duties. Her children were hungry! What could I possibly be doing that was more important than feeding her babies?

◆◆◆

That year's clutch grew by leaps and bounds and the hungry ducklings always needed more food. What a happy group! It was always such a delight for me to find them camped out on my doorstep. Just like their mom, Peanut's ducklings were very smart and this one group, in particular, extremely so. On their own initiative the teenagers split into two groups, one group guarded the back door and the other the front so that I could never leave the house without some goodies for them to eat.

The sociable little ducklings delighted all who met them. They followed everyone up my front walk, always trying to come inside with my company. And, of course, one day, as I opened my front door, they just strolled in. Mother Peanut was a bit apprehensive, but, the unflappable ducklings loved every minute of their visit. They checked out all the rooms, slid all over the tile floors, drank from my sweet Gypsy's water bowl, upset my blue-fronted Amazon parrot Pablo and my cockatiel Happy Bird and wreaked havoc all over my first floor!

Although I hate to admit it, I was sort of glad when Gypsy's collie-herding instincts surfaced and she took matters into her own paws, so to speak, first herding them into a tightly-knit group and then finally herding them out the back door. But, needless to say, we all enjoyed their visit immensely!

◆◆◆

One hot summer's day a few year's back, when Peanut was a young mother, there was a rare change in the weather - the temperature dropped almost thirty degrees in one day. Unfortunately, I was gone for most of the day and by the time I returned, it was dusk, very cold and raining very hard. It felt almost like a late fall day. I looked for Peanut and her babies, but, I wasn't too concerned when I couldn't find them. Peanut was such a good mother I just knew she had them tucked in somewhere that was warm and sheltered.

I fed all the ducks and was glad to finally be inside out of the chill. As I was trying to warm up, I heard a lot of clucking and fussing. I looked out my living room window and there was Peanut, bedraggled and anxious, frantically trying to help her seven little ducklings survive in this awful storm.

Unfortunately, they were at the stage where Peanut had just stopped brooding them which meant that because they no longer huddled underneath her, they were so much more susceptible to the extreme change in temperature. I knew Peanut was in trouble and I ran out to help as best I could.

I found Peanut trying to revive four of the ducklings and I was glad that she didn't know that her efforts were futile. At the same time, she was desperately trying to keep the other three surviving ducklings warm underneath her, but the ground was flooded and the ducklings were cold and wet and shivering uncontrollably.

Muscovy mothers are very protective of their babies and Peanut was the quintessential protective mama. I didn't know how I was going to be able to take the ducklings from her. I distracted her somewhat and, luckily, I was able to take the weakest of the three.

I ran back out in the pouring rain and somehow managed to bring in the other two. I tried not to look at Peanut who at this point didn't know who or what to be upset about and I hoped she would somehow know that I was trying to help her.

◆◆◆

Once inside, I was able to dry them and warm them up. They slept all night in my sunroom under lots of blankets with a light shining on them to keep them warm. I checked on them constantly during the night. They were doing fine - much better, I thought, than Peanut probably was. I knew that she would be searching all night, in the pouring rain, for her babies.

Sure enough, the next morning when I went outside I found Peanut looking all over for them. There is no more heartbreaking sight than that of a Muscovy mother looking for her babies and not finding them. Peanut looked in all their favorite places, gently cooing and clucking to them. Peanut came up to me pecking at my leg, practically begging me to join in the search. It was still too cold to give her back her surviving ducklings and my heart ached because I knew she would still keep looking. I felt so helpless.

◆◆◆

About two hours later, the sun shone brightly and the cold summer morning turned warm, The time had finally come for me to reunite the little duck family. The minute I brought the ducklings outside, they began to excitedly peep and, before Peanut could attack me, I gently placed them in the grass. What a joyous sight to see - the three little ducklings, peeping away, racing to their mama and Mama Peanut just cooing softly to them. Such a happy sight!

Did she thank me? Did she even "smile" at me? No and no again! Peanut just took her babies and happily marched away, but, I had all the reward I could ever imagine whenever I saw the four of them together in my garden.

The first rescued duckling, the one I thought would never survive, turned out to be a little horror. I named him Phillip. Whenever he was close to me he bit my leg for attention and, as he grew older, he continued this "bad" habit until I finally gave him his peanut. I guess nowadays I'd be called an enabler! I could, however, always easily tell Phillip apart from all the other white males - he hurt. But, he always made me smile!

◆◆◆

In 1998, in early June, Peanut's ducklings hatched a few days before a big engagement party I was happily giving in my garden for Tommy and Sharon, my oldest son and his lovely bride-to-be. I was concerned about Peanut and her new little family and I wondered how they would cope with all the guests, the caterers, the children, the music and the confusion.

Well, I need not have worried. I somewhat belatedly realized that Peanut had always considered my garden hers. Her routine that day only slightly changed, mostly to protect her little ducklings from the young children whose squeals of delight at the sight of the little black-and-yellow ducklings made everyone smile. Whenever Peanut decided it was time for her family to eat or to take a bath or to catch bugs, she marched them across my garden, around the tables, in between the guests and through the turmoil.

It was a lovely party with wonderful food held on a picture-perfect early summer day and the thing, not surprisingly, that almost everyone remembers is not any of that, but, rather, a very proud Peanut parading her ducklings around people, kids and caterers, just basking in the praise and compliments and, thoroughly, enjoying all the attention!

Chapter Seven

The "Diva" Duck ...

Grace was one of the most beautiful ducks I have ever had the privilege of knowing. She was smart and serene and her snow white feathers were always preened just so. I suppose that's why I named her Grace - just like the Princess of Monaco, my Grace was the "princess" of my garden.

Her daughter Patches, who was born in the summer of 1993, was nothing like her, either in looks or in temperament. As a duckling, Patches was black-and-yellow with big "patches" of each color, hence her name. When she grew up, the yellow patches turned to white.

And, in personality, Patches was nothing at all like her twin sister, Peanut. Patches was the original "duck diva," extremely theatrical, somewhat headstrong, a bit flamboyant and very definitely "high maintenance!"

Right from the beginning, I could tell that Patches was going to be a handful. Patches unquestionably knew she was meant to be a star ... a great star ... a mega star! And, I suspect, if she had a role model, it would have been Scarlett O'Hara. I could easily envision my extremely dramatic Patches living the life of luxury at Tara, boyfriends at her feet bewitched by her beauty and devoted servants catering to her slightest whim.

When Patches didn't get her way she threw temper tantrums. And, if ducks could "sigh," well, Patches' sigh would have been quite melodramatic. If I was unlucky enough to be nearby when she had a problem, she would march over to me, loudly whining, complaining and clucking a-mile-a-minute as she followed me around!

◆◆◆

A few summers' back, as Patches was crossing the road in front of my house, she was hit by a car. Fortunately, she wasn't hurt too badly, just shocked and traumatized. After I cleaned her up and took care of her cuts and bruises, I placed her in my hospital cage to recuperate.

Since Muscovies are very social and group oriented, I left the hospital cage outside all day to ensure that my patient would enjoy the company of her friends. Patches had many visitors but it was her best friend, Robert, who intrigued me. He sat by her side next to the hospital cage all day, every day, and didn't leave until it was evening and time for me to put Patches in the garage where she would be safe. Only, then, would Robert go down to the dock, where he'd push around a young Muscovy or two to get his favorite sleeping spot.

I suppose that was the beginning of their very special long-term love affair.

◆◆◆

Two years later, late one spring night, I spotted Patches in my neighbor's yard and I was absolutely horrified as I watched a red fox sneak up on her. She had made the lethal mistake of letting him get between her and the dock – a truly fatal error for her because she was unable to jump into the water for safety. I saw him grab her and

I saw her go limp in his mouth. And, to make matters worse, I saw Robert gallantly waddling as fast as he could after Patches and the red fox.

Worried for both of my ducks, I charged outside in my nightgown with Gypsy, my trusted collie, at my side. She and I chased the fox as far as we could along the fence line until he disappeared with Patches still hanging limply from his mouth and Robert trailing in the distance.

When I returned to bed, I couldn't sleep. All I could do was cry. Temperamental, flighty and ditsy as she was, Patches was still one of my very special girls.

◆◆◆

The next morning, I noticed Robert across the creek, sitting alone in front of an old building at the dredging company complex. He didn't move for almost two hours and I began to worry that the fox had also hurt him since the last time I saw him he was valiantly chasing after the fox trying his best to rescue Patches.

I took out my trusty binoculars and what I saw warmed my heart - truly, a sight I shall never forget - Robert sitting next to a bloodied, dirty, hurt, but very alive Patches!

Now, came the hard part. It was Saturday morning and the dredging company was closed. The only way to get to Patches was to drive around the creek to the opposite side. I knew that Chris, the owner of the boatyard next to the dredging company, would let me climb from boat to boat until I got past the boatyard and onto the dredging company property.

Ordinarily, not too difficult a task, but I had just had knee surgery. Although my orthopedist had told me to follow my usual routine, I knew that climbing around on unsteady boats was not exactly the "routine" he had in mind.

One of the workers at the boatyard kindly offered to assist me lest I fall in the creek and I gladly accepted his kind offer. We slowly made our way across seven boats of all sizes and shapes and finally arrived at the dredging company.

As I began to climb up to the dredging company's dock, I came across the very well-hidden spot where Mother Goose had chosen to make her nest. Since there was no way around, I had to climb right over her nest. To make matters worse, across the creek, I could see Father Goose pacing up and down on my dock, intently listening for a distress call from Mother Goose.

I climbed across Mother Goose very slowly and very carefully, speaking softly to her the entire time, fully expecting an imminent attack from her or Father Goose and easily envisioning myself falling in the muddy waters of the creek. It was heartwarming though to see just how much she trusted me as she allowed me to clumsily cross over her nest without so much as a ruffled feather.

Not the case for my helper from the boatyard – who I later learned had no love for the creek's resident geese. The minute he tried to step over Mother Goose's nest, Father Goose, who was watching from his vantage point across the creek, flew off my dock, in a veritable rage, honking as loud as he could, attacking and dive-bombing my "helper" who was, at least in Father Goose's eyes, the enemy. There was no way my husky "goose chaser" helper could get across Mother Goose's nest. Father Goose absolutely refused to stop attacking him until he retreated to the safety of the boat. Mother Goose and I had quite a laugh!

I had to go the rest of the way alone and I finally made it to a sad and worried Robert and an injured and exhausted Patches. I had no trouble catching her.

I think she knew I was there to help. Into my arms she easily came and then into the travel cage for the return trip home. Robert took the easy way - he just jumped in the creek and swam across!

Home at last! I was amazed to see that other than a deep bite on her neck which had stopped bleeding and was already clotting, Patches was not too badly injured. And, after a two-week stint in the hospital cage, of course, with Robert at her side every day, she emerged her usual dazzling and dramatic "diva" self!

I've spent a lot of time trying to figure out just how Patches escaped from the clutches of the red fox and, I've come to only one conclusion: Patches must have fainted or pretended to faint. I could only smile as I pictured my drama queen swooning - a la Scarlett!

It was probably then as the fox dropped her, most likely with wonderful visions of a delicious duck dinner floating around in his head, that Patches took flight. She is a swift and strong flyer and, I'm sure that she totally surprised the fox.

Patches did, however, learn her lesson. From that point on, at night, she stayed with the rest of the ducks on the dock and, from my bedroom window I could always see her snuggled quite comfortably next to her one true love, Robert.

Chapter Eight

Robert J.

Bridget, my veterinarian and friend, and I had a great mutually beneficial wildlife arrangement. She treated my injured wildlife and, in return, whenever one of her patients was ready to be released into the wild, but still needed some tender loving care, I took them home. They were free to come and go as they pleased and they quickly learned that breakfast and dinner – and sometimes midday snacks – were served daily.

And that's how Bianca came to me. She was a sweet, somewhat dirty, white Muscovy duck who was found, dazed and bleeding, wandering the railroad tracks in Westbury. Every time Bridget released her, Bianca could, once again, be found walking the same stretch of tracks. So, off it was, for this avian hobo, to Suffolk County, far away from the railroad tracks, to "Maria's half-way house" for ducks.

In nature's wonderful and romantic scheme of things, Bianca met Arthur, a rather dignified Rouen duck, and she soon became the mother of five - four little yellow ducklings, all the same size, and a much bigger black-and-white duckling and the only one with bright orange feet. I fondly called him my little "ugly duckling." But, just like in the fairy tale, I knew that one day he would be very, very special.

Right from the start he showed his distinctive personality– much to the dismay of his mother. It seemed that the little "big" duckling just didn't believe in following the "rules." All ducklings always follow their mother – everywhere - but this free spirit was the exception! When Bianca walked to the right, he walked to the left. When his mother and his four little siblings took a nap, he wanted to eat. When Bianca decided it was time for her ducklings to take a bath, he wanted to catch bugs on the lawn.

Bianca was beside herself, for no duckling had ever done this to her. Try as she might, she could not make him understand that this was very dangerous behavior for a helpless little duckling whose only protection lay in staying very close to his mother.

At first, Bianca gently nudged him and quietly spoke to him. When this didn't work, she began to cluck louder and louder. When that didn't work, she chased him with her four little yellow ducklings in tow. And, when she finally caught up with him, she angrily admonished him, fluffing up her feathers and, practically, stamping her webbed feet in a maternal tirade!

I could almost see Bianca pulling out her hair - excuse me, her feathers - as I once had done some years back. I couldn't help but smile, remembering my three sons, and thinking "I guess every mother has one." And, so, I named the adventurous, free-spirited, "bad" little duckling who never listened to his mommy, Robert James - Robert J. for short - after a brown eyed, curly-haired little boy who was the middle one of the three little loves of my life.

As Robert J. matured he became quite handsome - with beautiful black-and-white markings, deep blue eyes and bright orange feet.

Robert was a real charmer and quite a lady's man - a real smooth operator. In springtime, when a young man's fancy turns to thoughts of … well … so did Robert's. He chased all the girls, all the time, up and down the dock, in the water, through my garden, into the street. Wherever the girls were, Robert found them. He had only one thing on his mind and I won't go into that here!

◆◆◆

One summer, after all the girls were settled in their nests, Robert disappeared. I was devastated. I was certain that something terrible had happened to him and that one morning I would see him floating, stiffly, head down, in the middle of the creek, heading out to the eternal waters of the Great South Bay.

◆◆◆

In the fall, though, a very bedraggled Robert returned home. But, instead of receiving a warm welcome, Robert was attacked by all of the Muscovy girls. I had to warn them off with my straw broom, usually reserved only for overly-amorous males.

This happened year after year, until, finally, late one evening, as I was driving down the rarely used road at the end of the creek looking for Robert, I found my "street smart" duck, nonchalantly strolling to the local bar, Hogan's Goat, apparently, for drinks and dinner. He seemed completely at home, just hangin' with the locals, swaggering up to the barmaid and waddling over to anyone who showed any inclination to share their dinner with him.

Yet, for all of Robert's many indiscretions, he really had only one true love in his life, Patches, to whom he always returned.

◆◆◆

Over the years, the bond between Robert and Patches grew into something very special. They were inseparable. I could look out any window or go out any door and there, sitting under a shrub or luxuriating on the cool grass, were the lovebirds. Sometimes, they had their lovers' quarrels and one or the other would go stalking off into the creek. But, their anger didn't last very long and, once again, they'd be sitting side by side like a wonderful old married couple, content and happy just to be with each other.

Robert was the proverbial duck with "nine lives." A few years ago, I was awakened by the sound of flapping wings and loud frightened quacks. I ran to my front windows and there on my lawn were two huge dogs chasing my Muscovies, the mallards and Robert.

With the exception of Robert, all of the ducks could fly and quickly did so but Robert was trapped by the fence. One of the dogs, a boxer named Bailey, who lived across the street, grabbed a stunned Robert and was triumphantly taking him home.

Of course, by this time "Grandma Duck" was already out the front door in her nightgown - no robe - screaming at Bailey to "put Robert down!" School buses and cars were stopped while everyone watched in horror as Bailey made off with Robert. Fortunately,

Bailey's owner heard all the commotion, came out and took a very wide-eyed Robert out of Bailey's large jaws, whereupon Robert, ever the regal duck, straightened up with as much dignity as he could muster and limped across the street, totally oblivious to the traffic jam he had caused.

Robert slowly made his way into my backyard via an "entrance" I had cut out, years ago, at the bottom of my fence and he collapsed in utter exhaustion under my lilac bush. He lay there in the shade exhausted from his near-death experience, totally ignoring the cool water and cracked corn that I had quietly placed near him. He did seem to brighten up a bit when Patches came to sit by him, and, there, with the heavenly fragrances of lilacs and old roses wafting in on the warm air, the two lovebirds rested all day.

◆◆◆

The summer of 2000, took its toll on Robert and when he reappeared in the fall, he was a mess. He had lost a great deal of his feathers and the arthritis that he seemed to suffer in his legs, looked like it had gotten much worse. Robert was now seven years old and I truly didn't think he would make it to eight.

However, while never a really big eater, Robert was holding his own at feeding time - usually an excellent sign in wild ducks - and, I must confess, that I went out of my way to make sure that he had his own bowl of fresh water and corn. All I could do was hope for the best and be prepared to help nature help him if there was not going to be a happy ending.

◆◆◆

Wintertime, usually not that cold in recent years, was uncommonly cold, icy and snowy that year. In the midst of the first snowstorm, I went looking for Robert, food in hand, but, I couldn't find him anywhere. I feared the worst and, as the days went by with no sign of him, I started to lose hope. After four days the cold front passed and the sun finally came out - and so did Robert!

The heavy snow laying atop some of my huge ornamental miscanthus grasses down by the creek had flattened them into an almost igloo shape, and as the sun shone that happy day, Robert left the comfort of his newly-found home where he apparently had been toasty warm. I laughed at the thought of him all snuggled up and comfy in his "igloo" while I nearly froze to death looking for him!

Robert's feathers began to grow back and, before long, he was hangin' with his friends, Big Whitey, Patches and Peanuts, and, happily, it seemed that, once again, Robert had beaten the odds. Robert seemed to be the duck with the proverbial nine lives.

◆◆◆

Spring very slowly began to overtake winter and, as the days became longer, I could almost feel the spirit of rebirth and renewal in the air. That is, until I found Robert stretched out in my sanctuary. I tentatively called to him and I was so relieved when I saw him move. However, my relief was rather short lived. As Robert hobbled over to the food, he could barely put any weight on his right leg. I stayed with him making sure that no one would chase him away from his food. I knew that I had to take Robert to the vet, but, I also knew that capturing him would be no easy task. And sure enough, it wasn't!

I don't know how he did it but Robert always got away from me and my trusty fish net. A good sign, I thought, because the ease with which I can catch my wild-friends usually equates to the severity of their injury. I watched Robert swim away not knowing whether I was happy or sad or whether I would ever see him again.

Another two days passed without a sign of Robert. I drove around to the other side of the creek to ask the workers at the dredging company if they would please keep an eye out for Robert and, before I left, they conducted a thorough search for him, but, Robert J. was not to be found.

◆◆◆

The third day went by and still no sign of Robert. I checked across the creek again, but, no one had seen him. In my head, I unconsciously found myself planning a final tribute to Robert. I was sure the end had come.

The workers left at 3:30 that afternoon and, as I searched for Robert with my binoculars, I saw him under one of their big pipe trucks, still and stiff. I just couldn't bear for Robert to die such an ignoble death - all alone in a deserted yard underneath a dirty, rusty old truck. Then I breathed a deep sigh of relief as I saw his blue eyes open and his black head come up.

◆◆◆

More days passed and Robert still hadn't swum back across the creek to eat. Then out of the blue, one day, I walked into my sanctuary and there nestled between my flowerpots was Robert. And, as I gently walked over to him to see how his leg was doing, he just picked himself up - as if nothing had been wrong in the first place - and walked over to eat. And, when he had enough, he just ambled over to the dock, jumped into the creek and happily swam away.

◆◆◆

Later on, I saw him cavorting in the water with Patches. I could only shake my head with incredulity wondering just how many more lives Robert had?

Sadly, Robert J., my much-loved and charismatic wild-friend, crossed over the great Rainbow Bridge on May 28, 2001, accompanied by his best buddy "Big Whitey" ... I know Peanut and Gypsy were there waiting for him ... Godspeed, my little friend ... I will miss you so very much ...

Chapter Nine

Jack

My neighbor Jill did it to me again! Accompanied by her two children, Justin and Annie, and her brother's friend, Tom, and his two girls, she brought me a tiny little Muscovy duckling that was probably only a day or so old since his "egg tooth" - the tiny projection at the tip of a duck's beak that is used to chip the egg shell - was still very prominent.

Apparently, the little duckling had become separated from his mother and his siblings and was rescued by Tom as the little guy was being nipped and chased in the creek by the geese and the swans. The duckling was quite a handful and Jill thought that I might know to whom he belonged.

None of my resident girls were even close to having babies yet this year since many of their nests had been destroyed when the creek flooded during a major Nor'easter. And the unusually cold spell we had in the early spring didn't help any either.

My curiosity was very piqued. This was the first time that one of my girls hadn't brought her babies home.

◆◆◆

After Jill left and I was alone with the little duckling, I realized that Jill was absolutely right. This duckling was a real handful. He was like a little duckling on "speed," running everywhere and jumping off everything. I had no trouble at all naming him - Jack - as in "Jumping Jack!"

It was even hard to hold him. He squirmed and yelled. Most of the time new little ducklings like to cuddle on my shoulder and hide under my hair. I've always thought that it's probably the closest thing to their mother brooding them. And I liked the idea of my hair feeling like feathers.

But not Jack ... He wanted no part of relaxing, he just wanted to run and jump and cause trouble. It seemed that there was nowhere I could leave him - even for a minute - that was safe. He ran and jumped all over everything and everyone nonstop. Even Misty, with her puppy curiosity, ran away from him and she was smart enough to stay away!

Finally, in severe desperation, I went out to the garage and hosed off my trusty old pet carrier, the same one I had used for Peeper, and I took Jack up to the warmest place in my house, my third floor workroom. The minute I put Jack inside and closed the door, he began to peep and peep and peep. And, his non-stop peeping only continued to get louder and louder.

No duckling had ever escaped from my pet carrier so I knew Jack would be safe inside and I could go back downstairs to finish my chores. Downstairs, I could still hear Jack peeping. I tried to ignore him, but, try as I might, I couldn't. He peeped so loudly and so constantly that my mother's intuition told me to go back up the three flights of stairs to my workroom to check on him.

When I reached the staircase I was aghast. There was Jack, yelling with all his might, standing at the very top landing of my stairs, peering through the posts of my staircase, looking for all intent and purpose as if he were going to try to jump down the three flights of stairs into the center of my hard tile foyer.

I quickly ran up the stairs, grabbed him and went to check the carrier. I was sure that I must not have locked the door properly and that he had somehow managed to get it open. But, the door was locked tight. There was absolutely no way that Jack could have gotten out except to have squeezed through the tiny grating. No duckling had ever done that before. I could only hold my head and think "Whatever do I do with him now?"

At this point, I had to carry Jack everywhere because I was afraid to leave him alone anywhere. Together, we went down four flights of steps to my basement and found a great big IBM computer monitor box and I carefully put Jack inside. I brought him and the big box back up the four flights of stairs. Feeling that at last he was safe, I went downstairs to prepare dinner.

After about a half hour, I had a funny premonition and I went upstairs again to check on Jack. I couldn't believe my eyes, I looked in the box and he was gone. I looked everywhere, panicking. After what seemed like an eternity, I finally found him huddled in between some of my art supplies. I couldn't imagine how he had managed to jump out of this huge high box. I couldn't think of anything else to do but to tape the box flaps up making the box double its height. And, I could only hope that Jack wouldn't find another escape route!

◆◆◆

Jack spent a really peaceful night huddled under the towels, nice and warm, and in the morning, I was very relieved to find that he was still in his giant box. However, throughout the day, I began to notice that Jack acted very differently towards me than any of the other ducklings that I had raised. I supposed it was because I hadn't imprinted on him. He didn't follow me around. In fact, he had his own agenda and often ran away from me. I would usually find Jack nestled in one of my plants and I wondered if it reminded him of the happy hours he spent with his family.

I had the distinct impression that he was always searching for his mother and his brothers and sisters. And, tempting as it was for me to want to nurture a little duckling I knew that I would do my best to find his family for him for I realized that Jack's best chance of survival was to be with his mother.

◆◆◆

A week passed and I still couldn't find his mother. My heart ached for little Jack. He had quieted down so much that I really began to worry about him. I constantly checked his breathing. But, he seemed fine and I really felt that he was just very unhappy here with me. I knew that he wanted to be with his own family.

Once again, I went up to the end of the creek and around the other side looking for his mother to no avail. It was then that I realized that I hadn't seen one of my Muscovy girls, Laura, in quite a while. In fact, the last time I remembered seeing Laura, she seemed to be spending a lot of time at the end of the creek and I wondered if she was his mother.

Laura wasn't born here and she may have been raised as a pet so I think all the hustle and bustle of the other ducks was too much for her. Laura was given to me by and named after a wonderful Long Island artist and wildlife rehabilitator who had found the young duck sitting in the middle of her street. No matter how she chased her, Laura always went back to dangerously sitting in the middle of the road. Finally Laura-the-person captured Laura-the-duck and brought her to me.

I looked for Laura again at dusk, hoping to find her and her ducklings, but, she was nowhere to be found. The next day I searched again early in the morning, but, still no sign of Laura.

◆◆◆

That afternoon I drove around and, sure enough, Laura was at the end of the creek brooding her ducklings. They seemed happy and content and I noticed that a kind person had left a big pile of bird seed in front of the little duck family.

I raced home to get Jack, all the while wondering if my instincts were right. Would Jack be as happy to see his mother and brothers and sisters as I thought he would? And, would his mother recognize him as one of her own? And what if I was wrong? How would I be able to catch him and bring him back? And, if I had to bring him back to my house, how on earth would I ever keep up with him?

It's always so hard to return a little duckling to the wild, knowing all the things that could harm him, but, I knew that Jack's chances for survival were so much greater with his mother than with me. And, I knew deep inside that I was not only doing the right thing but the best thing for Jack.

When I brought Jack back to the end of the creek, Laura was still there with all her little babies. Jack immediately started to peep, something he hadn't done all day. I put him down on the grass about ten feet from his mother and he made a bee-line straight for her and his family. He ran as fast as his little legs would carry him. The other ducklings shied away, not knowing what this little yellow whirlwind approaching them at top speed was, but his mother knew. Laura clucked softly and gave him little pecks - I like to call them "duck kisses" - all over.

I left and, as I got in my car, I turned back to see Jack underneath his mom, cuddling with his brothers and sisters, happy to once again be with his family.

A happy ending for the little duck family and for me too! Seeing them reunited gave me that wonderful good-all-over feeling!

Chapter Ten

Ducky

Ducky had been some child's Easter present and, as so often and so sadly happens, the family had lost interest in the energetic little black-and-yellow duckling. As he grew from babyhood into a teenager, the little Muscovy was no longer cute and cuddly and he required a great deal of time and attention which they could no longer give to him. They were about to release him into a local pond ... which is generally a death sentence for a hand-raised duckling because the youngster hasn't learned the skills needed to cope in the wild.

That was the dire fate awaiting Ducky! I don't know if he knows how lucky he was and how close he came to an unhappy ending but, just in the nick of time, along came Ducky's adoptive "mom" who rescued him and brought him into her home where he happily grew up with his two "sisters" and his "dad."

Ducky's new family lived in Levittown. Built on what used to be potato farms, Levittown was the first and one of the largest mass-produced suburbs on Long Island and it quickly became a symbol of postwar suburbia.

Over 6,000 affordable homes were built for the returning veterans of World War II. In the late 1940's, a home in Levittown cost approximately $8,000, requiring a down payment of only $90.00. The community soon had its own schools, its own postal delivery, phone service, playgrounds, streetlights and community center.

The houses of Levittown have by now been so thoroughly expanded and modified by their owners that their original architectural form can be quite difficult to see. But the one thing that could not be changed was the fact that the homes were built close together on very small plots of land making Levittown definitely not the place to raise a teenage duckling – especially one who was an exceptionally strong flyer.

Ducky needed a place where he could be free, yet, still taken care of. He was almost fully grown and was quite mischievous and he had begun to "terrorize" his neighbors who were so afraid of Ducky that, sometimes, his "mommy" or "daddy" had to rush home from work to rescue them from Ducky's antics.

And that was when, just before Christmas in 2000, I received the frantic call from Ducky's adoptive family asking if I had room at the "inn" for another duck.

When they brought Ducky to me he was already a teenager. I could tell that his adoptive family had taken very good care of him. His feathers were so clean and shiny and since he now had his adult plumage and coloring - black and white with a beautiful touch of green - he just gleamed.

And the tears I saw in his "sisters" eyes, as they sadly said their goodbyes to the almost-fully-grown duck who had been such an integral part of their lives, told me that he was very well loved.

Sadly, the time had finally come for Ducky's family to release him - to let him be free - one of the hardest things to do when you have raised and nurtured a wild animal. His sisters slowly opened Ducky's cage and gently placed him down. My heart ached for them.

By now, we had attracted a rather large Muscovy audience on the driveway. And, as we stood talking and watching Ducky aggressively explore his new surroundings, I tried to prepare everyone for Ducky's initiation into Muscovy life explaining that, most often, the dominant males boldly assert their authority over a young male by chasing him around the garden, or, in worst case scenarios, chasing him into the creek. I stressed to the girls that the machinations of adjusting to the Muscovy pecking order always looked much worse than they actually were.

I continued to explain that most newly-released young males usually swim across the creek to the dredging company where they hang out for a few days until they either make peace, friends or get hungry enough to brave coming back. They then usually defer to the dominant males and life goes back to normal.

Not so with Ducky! When my big, old males tried to chase him, Ducky jumped on their backs and began fighting with them. He even jumped on Flora, my dominant female's back and began fighting with her! I'd never seen a newcomer act like this and neither did my other Muscovies. Ducky then belligerently marched down to the water, staked out his own territory and hung out on the dock alone.

As I expected, after about a week, Ducky found his niche in Muscovy society and things calmed down. Ducky now had a daily routine. He spent a lot of his time during the day swimming in the creek and, for a duckling that was not raised by the water and who only had a big "kiddie" pool to swim in he took to the creek like the proverbial "duck to water." I could see him from my windows happily splashing and cavorting in the creek.

When dinner time came, Ducky was no slouch. He pushed and shoved for his food, just like everyone else. Being "grandma duck," I was worried that maybe he wasn't eating enough. The weather was getting very cold and this, after all, was a new environment for him. Ducky was so friendly that I was able to pick him up and carry him to a more secluded part of my garden where I had placed a bowl of cracked corn just for him. Ducky took a few mouthfuls and left me without so much as a "thank you ma'am" and back he went to brawling with his new friends.

Ducky has already terrorized one of my young males who was born here last summer and, from time to time, I see him chasing some of the older males too! I have a feeling that he will climb, rather quickly, up the Muscovy ladder of success and, with his unique personality, will soon become one of the "web stars" on my website, Maria's Duck Tales.

◆◆◆

One early spring day, I watched from the window as Ducky had his first run-in with my sprinkler system.

The system had just been turned on and Ducky happened to be sitting on one of the rotary heads when it whirred out of the ground and a fountain of water came gushing out. Poor Ducky just couldn't imagine what was happening. He hissed at it, attacked it and then subscribed to that wise old proverb: "retreat is the better part of valor!"

◆◆◆

Springtime has finally arrived and, along with the sunny, warm weather, everyone has a case of spring fever. And, since we all know that "in spring a young man's fancy turns to thoughts of love," I'm glad to report that Ducky's thoughts have followed the appropriate paths and he now has a very pretty girlfriend.

Ducky's a little worn-out from fighting to protect his lady's honor, his feathers are a little askew and he has a slight limp in his right leg but he's none the worse for wear. He won all the fights and he now has the prize. I can hardly wait to see all the adorable little black-and-yellow "duckies!"

Chapter Eleven

Gardening with Ducks ...

I've always invited wildlife into my gardens and while the relationships, for the most part, had some give and take, until recently, things generally had gone rather smoothly.

Gardening with ducks, however, was quite different from anything I had previously known. I constantly had to make up new garden "game plans" and I soon learned that I had to be extremely flexible when dealing with a bunch of daffy ducks!

I don't know where to begin the stories of my gardening disasters - there were so many - but, I think, I'll start with my vegetable garden and the late Mrs. Whiney.

A little background: I raised three lively boys and always had their assorted and energetic friends romping through my small North Bellmore garden. I also had a succession of collies who loved to "herd" the squirrels through my small vegetable patch.

Additionally, since my twenties, I have had painful arthritis, particularly, in my hands and knees so kneeling and digging were always very difficult for me.

Those were several of the reasons why I started growing my vegetables in very large pots. I mixed my own combination of potting soil because its airy composition made it much easier for me to dig in. There were other advantages too. Because of the height of the pots I did not have to kneel and, since potting soil is sterile, there were no weeds to pull. Over the years, I had honed it down to an exact science ... or so I thought!

The ducks in my Bay Shore garden, however, showed me the true meaning of the word "adaptability" and I had to continually refine my "science." I learned my lessons well and I made my list of "improvements" to be applied the following year - as is always the case with gardeners anyway!

At first the ducks were afraid of my potted vegetable garden and that was just fine with me. But, unfortunately, there is always that one curious duck - the Christopher Columbus of "duck-dom" - and, once the "explorer" discovered my garden it marked the beginning of the end for me and my vegetables.

The ducks loved the tender green leaves and the tiny baby vegetables. All they had to do was jump up on the wide rims of the big pots and pig out. They ate everything in sight. And whatever they didn't eat, they sat on with their chubby little bottoms – rubbing the seedlings into the soil and into oblivion.

That was the first year!

◆◆◆

The second year I had several large, very high planters built for my vegetable garden. When designing the planters, my carpenter actually measured the height of the ducks – a first for him, I'm sure!

I took immense pleasure in watching my lovingly grown-from-seed, stocky little seedlings - tomatoes, peppers, eggplants, zucchini and basil – take root and begin to grow.

What I didn't realize was that the ducks were admiring the tiny vegetables in the new planters even more! I should have realized that something was up but, at this point, I was too new to ducks in my garden to appreciate their intelligence and ingenuity.

My tiny seedlings grew into little plants and then into bigger plants. They began to flower and then to set the tiniest of fruits and vegetables. My mouth was already watering for the taste of that first ripe tomato ... red and yellow heirlooms with basil and virgin olive oil ... Italian sweet, multicolored peppers slowly sautéed in olive oil ... grilled white and pink Rosa Bianca eggplants ... and, of course, my wonderfully aromatic zucchini bread which never tastes as good when made from anything other than my home-grown zucchini.

Unfortunately, for me, the Pekin's mouths were watering too! And all of those visions of baby gourmet vegetable "sugarplums" dancing around in my head were dancing around in their heads, as well!

◆◆◆

One early summer afternoon, as I was relaxing on my terrace, sipping a wonderful glass of wine and enjoying the serene sight and sounds of life on Penataquit Creek, I watched one of the Pekins - Mrs. Whiney - sitting in the nearby shade longingly studying my vegetable planter.

How idyllic, I thought: My garden growing, ducks napping under flowering shrubs and boats gliding past in the creek. Heaven for me!

I watched as Mrs. Whiney got up, stretched her chubby white body, preened her feathers a little, and began to stroll around. At this point, I had no clue how clever ducks could be and I was blissfully unaware that I was soon about to witness the error of my ways!

Regrettably, in the extensive calculations the carpenter and I had made for the planters, we had neglected to account for the fact that Pekins can fly a little and, much to my dismay, I quickly found out that a little flight was all Mrs. Whiney needed. A little jump from higher ground, a lot of flaps of her wings and there she was in my "duck-proof" vegetable planter.

I tried to gently chase her but she would have none of it. So, before she trampled my seedlings in her fright at being chased, I gave in and let her stay, resigning myself to the fact that, once again, I probably wouldn't get to eat any of my vegetables!

But devouring my vegetables was not what she had in mind. Mrs. Whiney just sat there watching the bees buzzing and butterflies fluttering. After an hour or so, she agilely - for a Pekin - jumped off my vegetable planter and left - without even so much as a glance back.

I got up and started to survey the damage which, surprisingly, was very minimal. That's when I discovered two perfect large white eggs nestled in a little depression between two of my tomato plants. Now, how could I, "Grandma Duck" - as I have, at times, been lovingly, I'd like to think, called - keep this soon-to-be mother from her child? The answer, of course, is I couldn't. After all, I told myself, what's a couple of tomatoes anyway? I could always go to our local farm stand. And, we do have wonderful ones on Long Island!

◆◆◆

Surprisingly, over the course of the next two weeks, Mrs. Whiney laid ten eggs in a beautiful nest lined with pine needles and some of the leaves from the more distant eggplant and pepper plants. None from the zucchini, though. I guess she thought the leaves too prickly for her delicate little chest. It was quite a sight, my mother-to-be sitting in the shade of two lush green tomato plants, quietly clucking duck lullabies to her babies who were still curled up in their eggs.

This went on for a week or two and, as I enjoyed this serene maternal scene, I almost convinced myself that the sight of ten little yellow Pekins running around my vegetable planter would more than make up for having to buy my vegetables at the farm stand.

Then, out of the blue, Mrs. Whiney had a change of heart. I don't know what happened inside her head. Maybe she was afraid of the responsibilities of motherhood - and, I'm sure, we could all sympathize with her a bit on that point - or maybe she knew that her eggs were not fertile and that there were no babies inside after all. I guess I'll never know what happened.

But suddenly, she voraciously ate the tomato plants which were shading her nest. She ate the basil which was growing in front of the tomatoes and then she polished off what was left of the peppers, eggplants and zucchini.

And then, without any explanation whatsoever, she just jumped off the vegetable planter and abandoned her nest. That night, sadly for me and for Mrs. Whiney, but, happily for Mr. and Mrs. Raccoon and their kids, I watched as the raccoon family hungrily polished off all the eggs, licking their fingers with great gusto!

That was the second year!

◆◆◆

The score was now Pekins: "2" - Maria's Vegetable Garden: "0". Definitely time for a new game plan!

Another year, another plan ... One hundred year old homes have rather unique features and my Dutch colonial was no exception. The old two-car garage was down by the water and the driveway was very long. It also had a swirl extension on the left side that was probably used to park additional cars. At any rate, whatever its long-ago use, I had no need for it now and decided to turn it into an innovative new vegetable garden.

I bought big new green plastic pots and netted the entire perimeter, tucking the netting underneath the heavy pots. And, to make it attractive on the outside, I bought a few large wine barrel planters for my hot pepper plants. Chile plants are not only edible, they make great ornamentals. And when the peppers mature in vibrant shades of red, yellow, orange and purple, they are absolutely breath-stopping.

◆◆◆

At this point, I was smug as a bug in a rug. I didn't have a care in the world. I just couldn't conceive of anyone bothering my fiery hot Chile pepper plants.

All went well until the vegetables began to ripen. I don't know how the Pekins did it but they hunkered down on the hard asphalt and wiggled their way underneath the weighted-down netting and right into my vegetable garden. That was bad enough but, once they were inside, they couldn't find their way back out. They frantically ran around the garden and caused a great deal of havoc to the plants trying to half-jump half-fly out.

I was terrified that they might seriously hurt themselves, so down came the netting and, in no time at all, gone were all of my beautiful vegetables.

I consoled myself with the thought that I would, at the very least, have a bountiful harvest of hot chile peppers ... although how many jalapenos, poblanos and habaneros can one lady eat or even give away?

I need not have worried. Just as I was about to harvest my peppers at the very peak of their ripeness, I went out one morning to find a few male Muscovies sitting in my pepper barrel planters demolishing every hot multi-colored pepper and every tender leaf. All that was left were the thick stems and, I'm sure, in time, they would have eaten those too!

That was the third year and the score was once again all in the ducks' favor. Maria's vegetable garden had yet to get on the scoreboard!

This couldn't go on. Surely, I was a lot smarter. I had to be ... at least, that's what I kept telling myself.

◆◆◆

Over that winter, I gave my vegetable garden a great deal of thought and, finally, I came up with a foolproof "duck-proof" plan.

Hundred-year-old homes not only have lots of unique features, they also have lots of nooks and crannies. And hundred-year-old Dutch colonials have faux porches over their sunrooms.

◆◆◆

In early spring, I turned the roof over the sunroom into my garden floor. I installed a special roof that could be walked on and watered. I replaced the skimpy railing with white lattice and I covered the new waterproof roof-floor with pebbles. I brought up all my pots and the requisite bags of potting soil, put in a water faucet and, voila, I had a fantastic "roof-top" garden.

As an aside, I have to thank my son Michael for

hauling all those buckets of pebbles and bags of potting soil carefully through my home and up two flights of stairs!

It was a great idea and, best of all, it worked. I had the most marvelous roof-top vegetable garden. The tomatoes grew through and over the lattice and, for years, summer visitors walking to the Bay Shore ferries stopped and marveled at the lush tomato vines that tumbled over the lattice and down the front of my home. I also grew peppers, eggplants and basil and had harvests that I still dream of.

And, trust me, I didn't feel one bit bad for the ducks!

Chapter Twelve

Billy Boy
and the ˜Ghost˜ ...

Pekin ducks are absolutely the funniest, raunchiest and rowdiest ducks ever to be hatched from an egg and I just love them!

♦♦♦

A few years back, my little colony of Pekins was down to just two males - "Mr. Whiney," the widower of the recently deceased Mrs. Whiney who had acquired that name because of her continual whining and complaining, and "Ghostie," a dashing Rouen male, who, notwithstanding his heritage and the difference in his coloring, considered himself to be a very dapper "man-about-town" Pekin.

Ghostie loved nothing more than to sprawl out on the grass, not moving a muscle, silently watching the world go by ... that is until a sweet young thing innocently waddled by. Then, like a bolt of lightening, Ghostie was up and on the move, chasing her all through my garden.

I can't tell you how many times I thought Ghostie had truly expired, especially when I'd find him sprawled on the grass with his head drooping in one of his many bizarre positions. I always walked over with a great deal of trepidation and stood over him for minutes, really believing he was dead. Then I'd see one eye ever so slowly open and then ever so slowly close as he realized it was only me and not some tempting "sweetie-pie."

♦♦♦

That particular spring started out as any other with every male duck's heart - amongst other things - turning to thoughts of l'amour on the lawn. There was one problem though this year: Mrs. Whiney and the other "ladies" were no more, having met an early demise at the rough hands of Ghostie and Mr. Whiney.

So that spring, with no girls to pursue, Ghostie and Mr. Whiney chased each other along the dock, along the lawn, along my garden paths, up on the terrace, down on the deck, just about everywhere. I think they kept hoping that one of them might suddenly reincarnate into a clone of the late Mrs. Whiney.

Totally frustrated, they even tried to whisper sweet nothings into the Muscovy girls' ears and that turned into a disaster for them. They got challenged by the powerful Muscovy males and, to make matters worse, the girls jumped on their backs, biting them, berating them, beating them up and doing awful things to their very sensitive male egos!

After watching their shenanigans for a few weeks, I couldn't take it anymore. I gave in to whatever "insane" whim possessed me and decided to take a trip out East to a duck farm where I knew that I could buy some new lady-friends for them.

It was quite an experience! I suppose that not too many people go to a duck farm nowadays to buy ducks to eat - let alone to buy girlfriends for their male ducks. However, once the owner of the duck farm heard my tale of woe, he became extremely enthusiastic. He even promised to pick out some beauties for the boys and he did - two all white, two black and whites and two beiges with some exquisite violet feathers!

Getting them home was quite a challenge. The owner of the duck farm had gently placed the girls in an old crate and, all huddled together, they began the long ride to their new home. Our "journey" only took about forty minutes, but, to me, it seemed like forty hours. Words cannot adequately describe the horrible smell in my Jeep - and that was with all the windows wide open!

Transporting the "girls" was truly a labor of love on my part. It was a very cold early spring morning, about thirty degrees outside, cloudy and dreary, damp with the anticipation of a cold drizzle. I was freezing and chilled to the bone but I couldn't close the windows or put the heater on in my Jeep because it would have just made the already awful smell that much worse.

Home at last! I put the girls, still in their crate, in the middle of the backyard to let them get used to their visitors who I hoped would soon become their new friends. After an hour or so, I opened the crate and waited for them to come out. It took a little while for them to get up the courage to leave but, finally, one by one out they came – all in a straight line and all in an unwavering row, a veritable tidal wave of Pekin girls!

And, so it went for days. What one did all five of the others did. Mr. Whiney and Ghostie and the Muscovies were all terrified of them.

Everyone ran away as the girls happily explored, making happy quacks at each new discovery. They waddled everywhere - except near the water - all in a line, all doing the same thing, always together. If one drank water all six did; if one ate cracked corn, all six did; if one decided to nap, all six did; if one ran over a sleeping duck, all six did. It was then that I lovingly nicknamed them "the dopies" (as in dumb).

◆◆◆

After a couple of weeks, the other ducks became less afraid of the dopies and the dopies, in turn, became less afraid of the water. Finally, one day I saw their fearless leader jump into the creek … although it seemed to me more likely that she tripped on one of the cleats on the dock and then fell into the water. All the other dopies, as usual, followed her, tripping over the same cleat and then falling into the creek!

Finally, at long last, their duck instincts kicked in and they began to really enjoy their swim-time in the creek. I loved watching them happily quacking and splashing, preening and ducking under the water and then flapping their wings wildly as they practically stood on top of the water. I could almost see the smiles on their funny little faces!

Up until now, Mr. Whiney and Ghostie had not only totally ignored the girls, but they had actually run away from them. But now that the girls were cavorting in the creek, the gleam was back in the eyes of ole Mr.

Whiney and Ghostie, for they both liked nothing better than long romantic days or nights on the water. They knew that they were faster in the water and much better swimmers than the girls who were just your basic "beginner duck" swimmers.

◆◆◆

Once in the creek, much to the dismay of the girls, Mr. Whiney and Ghostie very easily caught up to them and out-maneuvered them. But the girls learned very quickly how to avoid them. And, the girls suddenly realized that there were six of them and they quickly began using this fact to their advantage. After all the quacking and wild splashing stopped, I'd see an exhausted Mr. Whiney and Ghostie sound asleep on the dock and six wide-awake girls happily and peacefully playing in the creek.

Life on the land became extremely "lively" for the girls. Mr. Whiney and Ghostie relentlessly chased them everywhere. All day long and even sometimes late at night, I heard loud complaining quacks from the girls and the pitter-patter of duck feet running across the dock as the boys ran after them. They cared not who or what was in their way! They trampled my flowers, ran through my shrubs, hid behind my flowerpots but it was all to no avail. The girls rarely ever escaped the clutches of Ghostie and Mr. Whiney.

Even though the girls had been here for a while, I hadn't given them names yet. I always like to take time to watch my wild-friends develop so that I can pick a suitable name for their emerging diverse personalities. But, finally, one day – like a bolt of lightening out of the blue – their names suddenly came to me.

The girls were cavorting in their "pond" – a great big black plastic tub that was probably used to mix cement

– taking their daily bath when Mr. Whiney jumped in with something other than swimming on his mind. I was reading the newspaper and the headlines were all about the Bill Clinton-Monica Lewinsky scandal and I just couldn't resist.

Mr. Whiney got a new first name that day ... Billy ... and, finally, so did the girls ... Hillary, Monica, Gennifer, Flower, Paula and Joansie!

Chapter Thirteen

A Time for Tears ...
for Goodbyes ...
A Time to Move on ...

B *egun in Bay Shore on August 22, 2003 ...*

Once upon a magical time, my wild-friends and I lived happily on the shores of Penataquit Creek. I loved and laughed at the antics of the ducks and fed the swans in Nor'easters and blizzards. I was thrilled one summer by a pair of young ospreys as they attempted and re-attempted to build their first nest high atop a crane across the creek. And I was utterly captivated by the great blue herons and snowy egrets that fished for eels in the creek's shallow waters. I helped Mother and Father Goose in times of trouble and cried whenever one of my wild-friends didn't return.

Then, suddenly, like all magical moments ... one day ... it was so quickly gone. Sadly, it seemed, the time had come for me to leave this home I so loved. It was very simply time to move on.

For months, I had oh-so-carefully packed up all my treasures and, as I watched the heavy doors of the moving van close tightly, I silently turned away with tears in my eyes and an ache in my heart.

Alone now in the home I had loved for so long, all was empty and quiet. I allowed myself one final tear-filled look and then with my precious memories tucked tenderly inside my heart, while the words of an old John Denver song played in my head ... "How can I leave you again, I must be clear out of my mind" ... I gently closed the heavy front door for the very last time.

◆◆◆

Outside, I took a final walk through my garden and, with a very heavy heart, bade "Godspeed" to all of my very special wild friends who, for the past fifteen years, had so generously shared their lives with me.

Then with Pablo, Happy Bird and Kismet, my blue-fronted Amazon parrot, my cockatiel and my parakeet, all in their avian traveling cages and all perched precariously atop boxes stacked on the passenger seat of my SUV, and with an extremely upset three-year-old blue merle collie named Misty Blue, sharing the back seat with even more boxes, I very slowly drove away ... not daring to look back.

My home on Penataquit Creek had been more than just a house to me. It was my nest ... my sanctuary. Its ambiance was my creation and my garden was one in which I found an inner peace. It was supposed to be my "forever" home, the home I wanted to live in until the end of time ... the home I never wanted to leave.

And, as I slowly made my way towards Main Street, I told myself that by now, at age sixty-two, I should have learned that "never" doesn't always mean "not ever" and that "forevers" sometimes aren't meant to last a lifetime. That only happens in fairy tales ...

As I drove, I thought of all the things I'd miss and I reminded myself that I did get my wish – a special young couple had fallen in love with my home. She appreciated wildlife and was artistic, like me, and he was the kind of sweet guy that most mothers would love for a son. My home was in good hands and would be filled with happiness, warmth and laughter.

For my journey east, I did not take the busy main road, Sunrise Highway. That would have been too quick of a transition for me. I needed time to reflect and to understand the myriad feelings I was experiencing ... some so confusing and some so bittersweet.

And, as I drove along Montauk Highway on that perfect mid-August afternoon, I had to admit that there was a sense of excitement growing inside of me that, try as I might, I just couldn't deny. I've always loved the East End and it would be fun to discover new ponds to visit and new roads to travel. A larger woodland garden was waiting to be planted and new wild-friends were waiting to be made.

The previous October, I had stumbled upon an absolutely perfect-for-me piece of land located in a newly developed community in East Quogue. There were tree-lined winding roads where I could easily envision taking long walks with Misty and untouched woodlands for exciting adventures with my soon-to-arrive triplet grandbabies.

My very first look at what would soon be my new home, told me that the local naturalists must have fought hard – and had I lived here then I would have been right beside them – to keep these magnificent four-hundred-fifty acres that were a part of Long Island's precious Pine Barrens from being developed. I eased my conscience by telling myself that the land had already been cleared, someone would eventually live here anyway, and it might as well be me since, for the past forty years, long before it was popular, my gardens have always been wildlife habitats, the last two certified by the National Wildlife Federation.

My home would be one of the first of about one-hundred-fifty homes to be built on over four-hundred-fifty acres of pristine land. Approximately one-third of the interior land throughout the development was to be preserved as "open space." Abundant nature preserves also bordered the perimeters of the community.

Natural conservation buffers of oak and pine, twenty-five to fifty feet deep, had to be preserved around the perimeters of all properties. Old trees were respected and left standing and native species indigenous to the Pine Barrens of Long Island were to remain untouched in the buffers.

Covenants and Restrictions were also in place, protecting the natural beauty of the land and ensuring that there would be food and shelter for all native wildlife. I was thrilled to be part of this cutting-edge community that cherished the bounty of the land and the opulence of its wildlife and when finished, it would be this nature lover's dream.

Continued ... a few weeks later ...in East Quogue ...

It is now early September. I have somewhat unpacked and have finally begun to settle into my new home. For the past several weeks, my birdfeeders have been filled with sunflower seeds and cracked corn. My feeders are visited more and more and on some mornings they are completely empty, which is surprising since I fill them every evening. I have heard marvelous stories about the flocks of rare and unusual birds that visit the East End on their yearly migrations and I have begun getting up earlier and earlier to see who is emptying my feeders so quickly. Surely, it must be a very huge flock!

◆◆◆

And then one day just as the sun was about to rise, I stood transfixed for there, on my front lawn, was a doe with her young fawn. The graceful mother ate from the feeder and then knocked it back and forth so that the sunflower seeds and corn spilled out onto the ground for her baby. I was mesmerized and utterly enchanted as the little fawn ate and scampered around my front lawn tasting everything. And, then, he or she curiously came up to my library windows trying to figure out if my houseplants were edible too!

As I looked through my window into those incredibly curious and beautiful soft brown eyes, I couldn't help but wonder ... could I truly be that lucky again ... could the magic really be beginning anew?

Epilogue

Royal Rock Gypsy Blue

(Ch. Scotwarrior's Amadeus x
Royal Rock Black Crystal)

My remembrances of this very special time in my life would not be complete without mention of my sweet Gypsy Blue, my beautiful blue merle collie, who was such an integral part of my life in Bay Shore.

Gypsy loved to herd the ducks and she enjoyed barking at Diablo, albeit from a safe distance. And she always valiantly followed me whenever I went outside in the middle of the night to gently "encourage" the red fox to look elsewhere for his dinner.

♦♦♦

Sweet Dreams,
My Gypsy Blue

Written with deep sadness on May 25, 2000...

You came into my life one cold winter's day - a soft, warm bundle of blue-gray fluff with a happy little smile and silly eyelashes that were white on one eye and black on the other.

I loved you the minute I saw you and that moment was etched in my memory for eternity. You were so little, surrounded by all of your brothers and sisters, and, yet, even at that young age, you had your own unique personality. You wanted all of my attention, every minute. You excitedly climbed on top of your sisters and brothers to reach me for that very special "pet."

The night I brought you home the whole family was there waiting to welcome you. Most puppies would have been intimidated by so many people, but not you. You loved it, happily going from one set of arms to the next, quizzically looking into everyone's eyes wondering who would love you the most. You owned your home that night and all of the people in it! You knew it was your time to shine.

And as I watched you steal all of our hearts your name began to form in my mind ... you were my little "Gypsy" going wherever your heart took you ... wherever the love was.

We took long walks along the beach - just the two of us - only I was the one who walked! You always wanted to be carried and I more than happily obliged. One wintry day you chased the incoming tide but when you caught it, you didn't know what to do so you just plopped down in the icy ocean water. It was freezing outside and you were soaking wet. Your chubby little body was shaking so I tucked you inside my jacket and ran back to the car trying to keep you warm. I could never believe that one little wet puppy could fog up so many windows and make such a sandy mess in my car!

And then it seemed you grew up and I no longer had to protect you. You protected me from anyone and anything you thought was a threat to me. And yet, you humored me too. You had your own set of rules: outside animals, especially those pesky squirrels that I loved so much, could be chased, but inside was another story. How many hurt ducklings swam in your water bowl? How many climbed on you when you were asleep?

And then I helplessly watched as you grew older – a part of life's cycle that, try as I might, I couldn't prevent. I knew the time was fast approaching when I would have to prove my love for you - when I would have to sadly say good-bye to my very special blue girl. I didn't want to let you go.

But, suddenly, I no longer had a choice. I brought you to our very kind and compassionate veterinarian, hoping for miracles, but deep in my heart, knowing that none would be available. Age was against us. Much too soon, life had come full circle and the time had come, once again, for me to protect you, to see that you never suffered any unnecessary pain.

When I came to visit you for the last time, you heard my voice and your head lifted, your ears went up, and my broken heart shattered into tiny pieces. I held you in my arms and I kissed you and as I thanked you for the wonderful years we shared together, you put your dainty white paw on my arm, hugging me.

I looked into your sweet, gentle eyes for the very last time and even then you made it easier for me to do what I had to do - what was best for you. I could feel you saying "thank you"; "thank you for the good years and for not letting me hurt"; "thank you for letting me go peacefully ... for truly being my best friend."

And, then, my sweet cherished girl, I held you ever so tightly as you calmly went to sleep, cradled in my loving arms, for the last time. You left a pain in my heart that will never heal.

◆◆◆

Goodnight my beloved Gypsy ... You will always be there in that special place, reserved just for you, in my heart ... Sweet dreams my precious little girl ... till we meet again ...

Shortly after I wrote this, I received a private message in my Guest Book from a wonderful visitor to my website, Maria's Duck Tales. Her simple message which touched my heart deeply and brought tears to my eyes, asked if she could place a card for Gypsy at a memorial ceremony held by the Collie Club of America at Sunnybank, the former estate of Albert

Payson Terhune, the author of all of those magnificent collie books I had read and reread as a child.

And, so, on August 20, 2000, to the accompaniment of a lone Bag Piper playing "Coming Home," this very special collie breeder and collie judge lovingly placed my Gypsy's name, along with those of her own very special collies, at the foot of Champion Rock where all of our beloved collie friends are remembered each year.

My heartfelt thanks to you, Pati, for your empathy and kindness ...

About the Author

Maria Daddino writes "From Fourth Neck," a weekly community column published in the western edition of *The Southampton Press*. Her essays have appeared in *The Press Box* in both the eastern and western editions of *The Southampton Press*, as well as in *The Press of Manorville and Moriches*. Her wildlife stories have also appeared in the *South Shore Monthly*, the *Great South Bay Magazine* and *"In the Eyes of the Wild: An Anthology of Wildlife Poetry and Short Stories."*

Maria, a passionate gardener and wildlife enthusiast, invites and welcomes all wildlife into her garden. Her extensive native and natural garden, certified as a wildlife habitat by the National Wildlife Federation, has been on display in several East End garden tours. Maria lives in East Quogue with her collie Christy, her parrot Pablo and all of her "wild-friends."